INDIANS

BLACK HAWK, *Cleven*
OSCEOLA, *Clark*
POCAHONTAS, *Seymour*
PONTIAC, *Peckham*
SACAGAWEA, *Seymour*
SEQUOYAH, *Snow*
SITTING BULL, *Stevenson*
SQUANTO, *Stevenson*
TECUMSEH, *Stevenson*

NAVAL HEROES

DAVID FARRAGUT, *Long*
GEORGE DEWEY, *Long*
JOHN PAUL JONES, *Snow*
MATTHEW CALBRAITH PERRY, *Scharbach*
OLIVER HAZARD PERRY, *Long*
RAPHAEL SEMMES, *Snow*
STEPHEN DECATUR, *Smith*

NOTED WIVES and MOTHERS

ABIGAIL ADAMS, *Wagoner*
DOLLY MADISON, *Monsell*
ELEANOR ROOSEVELT, *Weil*
JESSIE FREMONT, *Wagoner*
MARTHA WASHINGTON, *Wagoner*
MARY TODD LINCOLN, *Wilkie*
NANCY HANKS, *Stevenson*
RACHEL JACKSON, *Govan*

SCIENTISTS and INVENTORS

ABNER DOUBLEDAY, *Dunham*
ALBERT EINSTEIN, *Hammontree*
ALECK BELL, *Widdemer*
CYRUS MCCORMICK, *Dobler*
ELI WHITNEY, *Snow*
ELIAS HOWE, *Corcoran*
ELIZABETH BLACKWELL, *Henry*
GAIL BORDEN, *Paradis*
GEORGE CARVER, *Stevenson*
GEORGE EASTMAN, *Henry*
GEORGE PULLMAN, *Myers*
GEORGE WESTINGHOUSE, *Dunham*
HENRY FORD, *Aird and Ruddiman*
JOHN AUDUBON, *Mason*
JOHN BURROUGHS, *Frisbee*
JOHN DEERE, *Bare*
JOHN FITCH, *Stevenson*
LEE DEFOREST, *Dobler*
LUTHER BURBANK, *Burt*
MARIA MITCHELL, *Melin*
ROBERT FULTON, *Henry*
ROBERT GODDARD, *Moore*

SAMUEL MORSE, *Snow*
TOM EDISON, *Guthridge*
WALTER REED, *Higgins*
WILBUR AND ORVILLE WRIGHT, *Stevenson*
WILL AND CHARLIE MAYO, *Hammontree*

SOCIAL and CIVIC LEADERS

BETSY ROSS, *Weil*
BOOKER T. WASHINGTON, *Stevenson*
CLARA BARTON, *Stevenson*
DAN BEARD, *Mason*
DOROTHEA DIX, *Melin*
FRANCES WILLARD, *Mason*
J. STERLING MORTON, *Moore*
JANE ADDAMS, *Wagoner*
JOHN PETER ZENGER, *Long*
JULIA WARD HOWE, *Wagoner*
JULIETTE LOW, *Higgins*
LILIUOKALANI, *Newman*
LUCRETIA MOTT, *Burnett*
MOLLY PITCHER, *Stevenson*
OLIVER WENDELL HOLMES, JR., *Dunham*
SUSAN ANTHONY, *Monsell*

SOLDIERS

ANTHONY WAYNE, *Stevenson*
BEDFORD FORREST, *Parks*

...*ryant*
...THUR, *Long*
...*nders*
...*Steele*
...*Stevenson*
...*tevenson*
...*ers*
...NE, *Peckham*
...*Monsell*
SAM HOUSTON, *Stevenson*
TOM JACKSON, *Monsell*
U. S. GRANT, *Stevenson*
WILLIAM HENRY HARRISON, *Peckham*
ZACK TAYLOR, *Wilkie*

STATESMEN

ABE LINCOLN, *Stevenson*
ANDY JACKSON, *Stevenson*
DAN WEBSTER, *Smith*
FRANKLIN ROOSEVELT, *Weil*
HENRY CLAY, *Monsell*
HERBERT HOOVER, *Comfort*
JAMES MONROE, *Widdemer*
JEFF DAVIS, *de Grummond and Delaune*
JOHN F. KENNEDY, *Frisbee*
JOHN MARSHALL, *Monsell*
TEDDY ROOSEVELT, *Parks*
WOODROW WILSON, *Monsell*

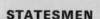

Eli Whitney

Boy Mechanic

Illustrated by Al Fiorentino

Eli Whitney

Boy Mechanic

By Dorothea J. Snow

THE **BOBBS-MERRILL** COMPANY, INC.
A SUBSIDIARY OF HOWARD W. SAMS & CO., INC.
Publishers • INDIANAPOLIS • NEW YORK

HARDEMAN COUNTY LIBRARY
QUANAH, TEXAS

COPYRIGHT © 1948, 1962, THE BOBBS-MERRILL COMPANY, INC.

ALL RIGHTS RESERVED

PROTECTED UNDER UNIVERSAL COPYRIGHT CONVENTION

AND PAN-AMERICAN CONVENTION

LIBRARY OF CONGRESS CATALOG CARD NUMBER: 60-7708

PRINTED IN THE UNITED STATES OF AMERICA

To my mother,
Theresa Moshier Johnston

Illustrations

Full pages

Numerous smaller illustrations

Contents

★　　★　　★

Books by Dorothea J. Snow

ELI WHITNEY: BOY MECHANIC
JOHN PAUL JONES: SALT-WATER BOY
RAPHAEL SEMMES: TIDEWATER BOY
SAMUEL MORSE: INQUISITIVE BOY
SEQUOYAH: YOUNG CHEROKEE GUIDE

★ Eli Whitney

Boy Mechanic

Crows in the Cornfield

IT WAS EARLY afternoon. The hot sun beat down on the back of young Eli Whitney. He was hiding at the edge of a Massachusetts cornfield in the year 1773, watching for crows. The crows wanted to eat the newly planted corn.

Eli was only seven years old, but old enough to drive away the crows. He looked up at the sky and saw a dozen crows coming. The sight of the crows made him very angry.

"Old mean crows!" he cried. "Old mean black crows! Old mean hungry black crows."

Eli dug his bare toes into the soft earth and waited for the crows to settle in the field. They made him very angry, but he knew that the corn must be saved.

This cornfield was very important to the members of the Whitney family. They would need the corn from this field for food during the next long, cold New England winter. The corn would provide roasting ears, hominy, corn bread, Indian pudding, and many other good things to eat during the winter.

Eli was wearing a new woolen shirt. This new shirt made his skin itch. Tomorrow he would wear an old shirt, which hung on a peg in his bedroom. The old shirt had been washed so many times that all its prickly spines had been worn away. How much better it would feel than this new scratchy one!

"Tomorrow when Father calls," Eli promised himself, "I shall get up right away. Then I'll have time to make sure I put on the right shirt to wear in the sun."

Now the crows were circling the cornfield
again. Down, down, down they came.

Eli waited until their claws almost touched
the ground. Then he sprang to his feet and ran

along the rows of corn, yelling "Yaaaa—. Get out of here. Get out! Get out!"

Swoosh went the crows. With angry squawking, they took to the air. They did not like the boy who came running after them.

Eli ran to the spot where the crows had come down into the field. Some of them had been successful. On the ground lay several tender green shoots, uprooted by their bills.

"Robbers!" Eli cried, shaking his fist after the birds. Then he trudged back to his spot at the edge of the field. "To think they pull up whole plants," he muttered. "All they want are the kernels at the roots."

Eli crouched again. He picked up a handmade, single-bladed knife that he had thrown down a few seconds before. Also, he picked up a piece of red-cherry wood from which he was carving a butter paddle for his mother.

He looked again for crows in the sky.

14

"How can I finish this paddle for Mother's birthday, if I have to spend all my time chasing crows?" he said.

He cut a few paper-thin shavings from the paddle. Then he held the paddle at arm's length carefully to look at it.

"Caw, caw, caw!" Alas, the crows were coming again. Eli made ready to spring, and the crows left almost at once. This time he had been too fast for them. They had not uprooted a single plant in the cornfield.

Again and again Eli chased the crows from the field. Again and again they returned. The afternoon passed slowly.

Eli stayed in the field until dusk. Then he heard his father's whistle, sharp and clear, calling him to come home.

"Glory be!" he exclaimed as he started on a run for the house. "Now I can get rid of this scratchy new shirt on my back!"

15

"Eli! Eli! It is five o'clock," called Eli's father early the next morning.

Eli got up promptly. He reached for his old shirt, and put it on quickly. Then he slipped into his old trousers and drew the belt string tight about his waist.

As he hurried down the stairs, he thought of the dream that he had had the night before. He had been carrying a cage full of crows.

Oddly enough, the crows had been able to speak English. They had called him a mean boy, and he had answered, "Caw! Caw! Caw!"

"What are you grinning about?" asked Betsey, his younger sister, when he reached the foot of the stairs. "What is so funny about watching crows in the cornfield?"

"There's nothing funny about watching crows in the cornfield," said Eli. "It is catching them that makes me smile."

16

"Who would want to catch a crow, and what would he do with it?" asked Betsey.

"Umm!" sniffed Eli. "We are having pancakes for breakfast!"

Eli and Betsey raced to the kitchen. Their father and small brother, Josiah, were already seated at the long, narrow table. Their mother was busy baking the thick, fluffy pancakes for them to eat and to enjoy.

"You seem to be ready for another day in the cornfield, Eli," said Mrs. Whitney, placing a sizzling pancake on his platter. "I'm certainly glad that you put on your old shirt today. It's too hot to wear a new shirt."

"You surely are right about the shirt, Mother," said Eli. Then he picked up the sugar box and sprinkled sugar over his pancake. "I'll be glad when the corn gets too big for crows to bother," he added with a sigh.

"Watching crows may not be the nicest job on

the farm," said Mr. Whitney, "but it is necessary. Without the corn there would be much less to eat in the winter."

"Thinking of food makes the job of watching easier," Eli agreed. Suddenly he asked, "Do you think a cage full of crows, hung in the cornfield, would scare other crows away?"

Everybody laughed. They didn't seem to think much of Eli's idea.

Mr. Whitney raised one eyebrow. "Well, it might make the crows afraid," he said.

Eli didn't seem to notice the amusement on everyone's face. He turned his attention to the pancake he was eating.

Soon Mr. Whitney rose from the table. He said, "The crows are up, Eli. I heard them cawing when I came from the barn."

Eli finished his last pancake. Then he started for the field. He hadn't gone far when he stopped short to think for a moment.

Crows in a cage! Well, why not? He could catch a rabbit in a basket trap. Why couldn't he catch a crow?

"It's worth trying," he said.

He went back to the hedge by the lane and hid quietly until his mother and Betsey went to feed the chickens. He waited until his father went to do the chores in the barn. Then he went on toward the house.

"I'll take both a basket and a bird cage," Eli said to himself.

He stopped at his father's shop, a small stone building about ten feet from the house. The shop was filled with many kinds of tools. In one corner stood a big forge and anvil. Close by was a long bench with a vise and wood-turning lathe. The table was loaded with hammers, saws, chisels, and files.

Mr. Whitney made furniture for the house and made or repaired all the equipment on his farm.

He also made or repaired many things for other people in the community.

The shop was a favorite spot for Eli. He spent every moment that he could during the day there. He liked tools and looked forward to the time when he could use them himself.

Eli knew where everything was in the shop. He took down a bird cage that hung from the ceiling and picked up a large basket, filled with shavings, at one end of the bench. He poured the shavings from the basket and put the bird cage inside. Then he slipped out of the shop, ready to get some bait for his trap.

Mr. Whitney had some ears of corn in the attic of the house. Eli knew where the corn was in the attic. Quietly he ran up the stairs and picked up several ears.

A few minutes later, panting, he reached the cornfield. He was just in time. The first crows of the day were heading for the corn.

CAW! CAW! CAW!

Eli ran up and down the rows of corn, waving his arms and yelling. He drove off the crows. Then he set to work on his trap.

He placed the basket upside down in an open space between the cornfield and the fence. Then he propped the basket up on one side with a small forked stick.

Next he took an ear of corn from his pocket, and shelled a handful of kernels. He started about ten feet away and sprinkled kernels all the way to the basket. Also he placed a small pile of kernels under the basket to coax the crows into his trap.

Finally, he tied one end of a long string to the bottom of the forked stick. He held the other end in his hand, and hid behind some berry bushes a short distance away.

Soon six or eight crows swooped down and began to eat the trail of corn. Some of them seemed to start eating the pile of corn under the basket. Then Eli quickly jerked the string and away flew the crows. He had pulled the string too soon and frightened the crows away.

Eli made another trail of corn to the basket. The crows came, ate the corn, and flew away. Not one went under the basket.

Eli made another trail, and another, and the same thing happened. Finally he was down to his last ear of corn, and still he hadn't caught a crow under the basket.

He shelled the last ear and made another trail to the basket. The crows came. They swooped down. They ate right up to the edge of the basket. There they stopped short.

Suddenly something happened! One crow, a little braver or greedier than the rest, stepped under the basket. He saw the big kernels that lay there and wanted to eat them.

Quickly Eli pulled the string and down came the basket, with a crow underneath. The crow began to squawk and squawk.

Eli jumped up and ran for the basket. He whooped for joy and danced around the basket, thumping the bottom. "I have you now, you mean old greedy black crow!" he shouted.

Only a flutter of wings and a frightened squawk answered him. Suddenly he stopped dancing and began to think about putting the crow in the cage. He must hurry, because he wanted to use this crow to scare the other crows away. Soon the other crows would be coming.

Eli brought the cage close to the basket, and lifted the edge of the basket, ever so carefully. He reached under the basket as far as he could, but he couldn't reach the crow.

He lifted the basket a little higher, but still he couldn't reach the crow. Finally, he poked his head and shoulders under the basket, and grabbed for the crow.

Swish! Out came the crow like a flash. Eli lunged forward to catch it, but it got away. Then Eli fell flat on his face and down came the basket on top of him.

Just then Eli heard a giggle, and there beside the basket stood his sister Betsey. "Your trap didn't work," she laughed. "You were the one who got caught."

Eli pressed his lips together tightly. He didn't want Betsey to see him cry.

"I came to bring you your lunch, and I have many good things for you to eat," Betsey went on in a kindly voice. She gave him two thick slices of well-buttered bread, and a big piece of yellow cheese wrapped in a napkin. Also, she gave him a small jug of milk. Then she said, "Good-by," and was gone.

Sadly Eli sat down and unwrapped his lunch. As he began to eat, a big tear trickled down his cheek. Already he had used up all his corn, but he hadn't caught a single crow.

"Caw! Caw! Caw!" The big black crows were still calling from the treetops.

A New Helper

At breakfast several days later Mr. Whitney said, "I think I'll go to Boston today."

Mrs. Whitney gasped. Eli dropped his spoon. Betsey sat open-mouthed. They couldn't have been more surprised if Mr. Whitney had said he was going around the world.

"My work in the shop leaves me little time to work on the farm," he explained. "We need help on the farm, and there are few able-bodied men to hire around here."

"I know," Mrs. Whitney nodded. "All the men around here have their own farms."

"That is right, but I believe I can find someone

in Boston," said Mr. Whitney. "Besides you have a birthday coming soon, and I can find no suitable gift for you in Westboro."

Mrs. Whitney smiled.

"I shall be gone only a few days," said Mr. Whitney to Eli. "The flax is ready for weeding. Weed it while I am away."

Eli's heart sank. How could he weed flax and finish the butter paddle in time for Mother's birthday? He would have to work on the paddle when he was resting from weeding.

Soon Mr. Whitney rode off. Eli left for the field of flax.

"I'll come to help you after I finish churning," his mother called after him.

Eli's heart sank again. How could he work on the paddle with his mother around?

He carried a pair of long woolen stockings to wear in the field. The stockings would keep the thistles from scratching his legs.

Eli reached the field and found an inviting shady spot under a tree at the edge of the field. He sat down under the tree and started to whittle. His mother wouldn't come for some time yet. The flax could wait.

An hour later he looked up and saw his mother coming. Quickly he hid the paddle and knife and stepped into the field. He was weeding busily when Mrs. Whitney arrived.

At once the thistles began to scratch his legs. In his haste to start working, he had forgotten to put on his stockings.

"Why, Eli!" exclaimed his mother. "How can you weed without wearing your stockings? Don't the thistles hurt your legs?"

"Yes, a little," said Eli. "I forgot to put on my stockings, but I think I'll stop now and put them on."

Flax was a valuable crop to raise on the farm. The best fibers were used in making linen, and coarse fibers were used in making rope. This kind of rope was very strong.

"It's hard to believe that flax can be used in making something as smooth as linen," said Eli. "I like linen cloth."

Mrs. Whitney straightened up from her back-breaking task. "We should have a good crop of flax this year," she said. "If we do, I know what I shall do with some of the linen."

"What, Mother?" asked Eli, glad for a chance to stop working.

His mother smiled. "I'm going to make you a linen shirt," she replied.

Eli's eyes grew big and round. "Only wealthy boys wear linen shirts!" he gasped.

"Then my son shall be wealthy," she said.

Eli worked faster now. For a long time he had wanted a linen shirt. Perhaps this old flax field was a good thing after all.

Suddenly Eli asked, "May I have a red-and-white checked shirt, Mother? I've always wanted a checked linen shirt."

"Yes, if I can get some red dye to color the red threads," laughed his mother. "I will try hard to get the red dye."

Weeding no longer seemed to be a chore for Eli. Not if it meant getting a red-and-white checked linen shirt to wear.

RICHARD FOLKES

At sunset, three days later, a horse with two riders came up to the Whitney farmhouse. Eli and Betsey ran out to meet them. "Hello, Father," they called.

Mr. Whitney jumped from the horse to greet the children. The second rider slid off and stood quietly at one side.

"This is Richard Folkes," Mr. Whitney said. "I know that you children will like him. He will

work for us for three years to pay off a debt. He is a redemptioner."

Eli had heard of redemptioners, persons who agreed to work for a few years to pay their debts. He wondered what kind of person Richard really was. What had he done to be in debt? Was he a person to be trusted? He didn't look like a person who had done anything wrong.

Mrs. Whitney came from the house to greet the newcomer. Then she and Betsey hurried to prepare the evening meal.

"Come, Richard," said Mr. Whitney. "Before it grows dark, I'll show you some of the farm. Then you can see where you'll work."

Eli tagged along behind his father and Richard. He was curious, and wanted to hear everything they had to say.

When they returned to the house, Eli noticed that the table had been set for six people. "Is Richard going to eat with us?" he wondered. "It will seem funny to have a strange person sit at the table with us."

Mr. Whitney asked Richard to sit at one end of the long table. He ate a big meal. Eli kept watching him.

Soon Mr. Whitney pulled something shiny from his pocket and looked at it. It was something he had bought in Boston. Then he took out a key and began to wind it.

"Oh, a new watch!" cried Eli. "Father has a pretty, new watch!"

"I can hear it tick!" cried Betsey.

"It's round and shiny!" said little Josiah.

"I am glad, dear," Mrs. Whitney said, "that you bought something for yourself."

"I've always wanted a watch," Mr. Whitney said. "I shouldn't have spent the money, but I'll enjoy having a small timepiece."

Mr. Whitney put the watch back into his pocket. Then everyone soon forgot it, except Eli.

33

He wondered whether winding made it tick. What made the hands move at just the right speed to show the time by hours and minutes?

After supper the family gathered around the fireplace. The evenings were chilly, and a fire burned all the time. Richard tried to make friends with Eli, but Eli shied away.

Just before bedtime, Eli whispered to his father, "Are you going to lock your shop tonight before you go to bed?"

"Why should I lock the shop tonight?" asked Mr. Whitney in surprise. "We have no thieves in this neighborhood."

Eli looked about to make sure no one was listening. "I'm afraid Richard might run away with some of your tools," he whispered.

"What makes you think Richard would do anything like that?" asked Mr. Whitney.

"He's a redemptioner, and redemptioners can't be trusted," said Eli.

A smile played about Mr. Whitney's mouth. "Who told you that kind of story?"

"Billy Burkett," replied Eli. "He told about a redemptioner who robbed stagecoaches."

Mr. Whitney started to laugh. "Billy's story may be true," he chuckled, "but all redemptioners are not criminals."

"Redemptioners are persons in debt," Mr. Whitney went on. "Many of them are very fine people. Some of them grew up in England, and went in debt to pay their way to America. Richard went in debt to pay his way to America."

"How much did he go in debt?" asked Eli.

"Nine pounds," replied Mr. Whitney.

Eli didn't know much about money, but he knew that nine pounds was a big debt. If Richard were worth nine pounds, he must be good.

After this little talk with his father, Eli quit worrying about Richard. He went to bed and slept peacefully all night.

Eli awakened and dressed early on his mother's birthday. He was glad that he had thought about making a butter paddle for her. He could hardly wait until evening to give it to her.

He ran to a secret hiding place in the chest beneath the window and pulled out the paddle. It was a beautiful paddle, strong and gracefully shaped. By snatching moments every now and then, he had managed to finish it.

"This handle is as smooth as a wet pebble," he thought. "It won't rub blisters on Mother's hand as the old one did. I'm glad I scraped it with a piece of glass."

He laid the paddle gently back in the chest and covered it carefully to hide it. "I wish that it were suppertime right now," he said to himself. "That's when we are going to surprise Mother and give her our birthday gifts."

Mr. Whitney had asked Richard to call Mrs.

Whitney outdoors just before everyone sat down to the table for supper. Then everyone would put their gifts on the table.

A few minutes later everyone sat down in the kitchen for breakfast. Mr. Whitney started to drink a strong cup of tea. Suddenly a surprised look came over his face.

"Where did you get this tea?" he asked. "It tastes very strange."

"I made it from raspberry leaves," replied Mrs. Whitney. "I didn't make real tea, because I didn't want to pay the tax on it. The British charge a tax on all the tea that we buy."

"You are right," answered Mr. Whitney, "and we shouldn't have to pay the tax."

"I'm glad that I don't drink tea," said Eli. "The British haven't started to tax milk yet, so I can drink milk."

Betsey and Eli helped Mrs. Whitney to clear away the dishes. Soon Richard came in with a bucket of milk, which he placed on the table. "I think it will rain," he said.

"Oh, dear, I hope not," said Mrs. Whitney. "Today is wash day, and I want my clothes to have a chance to dry."

Mrs. Whitney went to the mantel and took down a paper-covered book called *Poor Richard's Almanack*. This book was supposed to tell what the weather would be like.

"The *Almanack* shows sunny skies for today," said Mrs. Whitney. "What shall I do about my washing today?"

"Put it off until tomorrow," answered Eli. "You can't believe the book."

"You scamp!" laughed his mother. "Run along and help Richard hoe the corn."

That afternoon big, dark clouds started to gather in the sky. The wind began to blow harder and harder. Then rain came, first in large drops, then in dashing streaks.

"We had better run to the house as fast as we can," shouted Richard.

The two of them started to run, but they were drenched before they reached shelter. The skies opened, and the rain poured. Water gushed into ditches and gulleys.

"I am glad that I didn't wash today," said Mrs. Whitney, setting the table for supper. "I wonder whether I can wash tomorrow."

"I think that you will be safe in washing tomorrow, Mrs. Whitney," said Richard. "If you will step outside, I will show you why."

Mrs. Whitney went outside and Richard showed her a beautiful rainbow in the sky.

"I think you are right, Richard," she said, looking at the beautiful rainbow.

"A rainbow at night is a sure sign of fair weather the next day," laughed Richard.

Little did Mrs. Whitney realize what was going on inside the house. Everyone was busy, getting ready to surprise her with birthday gifts when she entered the kitchen.

When Mrs. Whitney went back into the house, she found the table loaded with birthday gifts.

There was the red-cherry butter paddle from Eli and special gifts from Mr. Whitney and Betsey and little Josiah.

"I am sorry that I have no gift for you, Mrs. Whitney," said Richard.

"You really gave me a gift when you kept me from washing today," said Mrs. Whitney. "Now my clothes will have a chance to dry."

The Fall
of the Year

IT WAS A CLEAR, crisp day in October. The rolling hills around the Whitney farm were no longer green. The leaves on the trees had turned yellow, red, and brown.

The harvest during the year had been very good. Mr. and Mrs. Whitney were happy, because there would be plenty of food for both family and livestock during the winter.

Eli and Betsey were busy hunting oak leaves for use during the winter. They were picking up leaves and piling them under a tree.

Mrs. Whitney would use some of the leaves for baking bread during the winter.

"Umm," said Eli. "I can hardly wait to eat some of Mother's good bread this winter." He could almost smell the crusty loaves that she would bake under the leaves.

"All you think about is eating," said Betsey, continuing to pick up leaves.

"That isn't so," said Eli. "When I am asleep I don't think about eating."

"Perhaps not," said Betsey, "but when you dream, I'm sure that you dream about eating. Come now, let's gather all the leaves that we can while we are here."

"Mother wants us to find a small birch tree for making a broom," said Eli. "She wants a new broom for winter."

A few minutes later Betsey called, "Here is a fine little tree for making a broom."

Eli ran to look at the tree. "Yes, this is a good tree, but how thick is it?" he asked, drawing a string from his pocket.

"What are you going to do with that piece of string?" asked Betsey.

"I'm going to measure the tree to see whether it is thick enough," said Eli.

Eli put the string around the tree. Then he held this part of the string together, and folded it into three equal parts.

"One-third of the string will tell me how thick the tree is," he said.

Eli measured the folded string with a small piece of wood that he carried in his pocket. He had the stick marked off in inches to use as a measuring stick.

"This tree is just the right size for making a broom," he said. Then he placed three small stones by the small birch tree, so that he could find it later.

Just then the children heard the clop, clop, clop of a horse's hoofs. "I wonder who is coming to see us?" cried Eli.

Eli and Betsey ran from the woods and looked down the road. There came Billy Burkett's father, riding horseback.

"Hello," said Mr. Burkett. "Are your father and mother at home today? I have some important news for them."

"Father is working in his shop and Mother is weaving," answered Eli. "You will find both of them at home."

Mr. Burkett flicked his whip, and the horse started away on a trot.

Eli and Betsey were eager to find out what important news Mr. Burkett had for their parents. Finally they decided to carry some leaves to the house to find out.

Mr. Burkett was talking with Mr. Whitney in their father's shop. The children paused and heard Mr. Burkett say, "Yes, we plan to have a husking bee in our barn Friday evening. We want all of you to come."

Betsey and Eli looked at each other, happy to learn about the husking bee.

"Isn't it strange," asked Eli, "how much more fun people think it is to husk corn at a bee than it is to husk corn at home?"

"That's exactly why people have husking bees!" laughed Betsey, as the children started back to the woods to gather more leaves.

THE HUSKING BEE

On the day of the husking bee, Mrs. Whitney and Betsey worked hard preparing food for the bee. Each family had to bring a share of the food for everyone to eat.

Eli could hardly wait to get started to the husking bee. He thought that the day would never pass, but at last the family climbed into a carriage, ready to go. Richard planned to follow the carriage on horseback.

"I'm afraid that we are going to have a storm tonight," said Richard regretfully, as he started to mount his horse.

Eli and Betsey were very unhappy about Richard's remark that a storm might be coming. They were afraid that their parents would decide not to go to the husking bee!

"Why do you think we are going to have a storm?" asked Mr. Whitney.

"When the wind is in the east, it is good for neither man nor beast," replied Richard.

Eli wet his finger and held it up. The wind was straight from the east.

"Let us look at *Poor Richard's Almanack*," said Mrs. Whitney.

Mr. Whitney rushed into the house to look at the *Almanack*. Soon he came back, saying that the weather would be clear and colder.

"I'll get another blanket," he said. "Then we'll be on our way."

When they pulled up in front of the Burkett farmhouse, Billy ran out to meet Eli. Soon the Whitneys were part of the happy, laughing crowd in the barn. The barn floor had been thoroughly cleaned and covered with fresh straw. There were two piles of unhusked corn, one at each end of the floor.

"We will draw to see who will be captains of the two teams," said Mr. Burkett, holding up a small bunch of sticks, covered at one end. "The two men who draw the shortest sticks from the bunch will be captains."

The men picked out sticks. Mr. Hawks drew the shortest stick in the bunch and Richard the next shortest stick.

"Choose your men!" cried Mr. Burkett.

Mr. Hawks called, "Mr. Adams!" Then Mr. Adams stepped over beside Mr. Hawks.

Richard chose Mr. Whitney, and Mr. Hawks chose another man, and so on.

Eli sat wondering whether either captain would choose him to husk corn. Soon he heard Richard call, "Eli Whitney!"

"Now," said Mr. Burkett, "the team that finishes husking first wins the prize."

"What is the prize?" someone asked.

"A knitted water-bucket!" laughed Mr. Burkett. "Ready, get set, go!"

Strong brown hands began to tear the husks from the ears of corn. Suddenly a boy shouted, "I have a red ear! Now I can kiss a girl!" He ran to a girl and kissed her.

Several other huskers found red ears. Eli hoped that he wouldn't find any. He didn't want to kiss a girl. Then suddenly he looked down and he held a red ear in his hands!

The men roared with laughter. "Kiss a girl!" they shouted. "Kiss a girl!"

Eli swung around and kissed someone, but he didn't know whom. He had kissed a boy!

The crowd roared with laughter. "Eli is afraid," they shouted. "Eli is afraid of girls. Eli likes to kiss boys."

Eli's face turned as red as fire. He hardly knew what to say or do. For a moment he stood hanging his head. Then suddenly he ran over to a girl and kissed her.

Again the crowd roared with laughter. "Eli likes girls, too," they said. "Eli likes to kiss girls as well as boys."

Now Eli was beginning to feel better. Soon he burst into a laugh, too, but he didn't know why. Was he laughing because he had kissed the boy or because he had kissed the girl?

The husking bee went on and on and everyone had fun. Several other huskers found red ears before the evening was over, and all of them kissed girls. Eli hoped that he wouldn't find another, and he didn't.

Richard's team won. Each member received a

big, red apple. Eli began to eat the crisp fruit. Juice dribbled down his chin, but he felt happy. Apples tasted better at husking bees.

ELI'S NEW FRIEND

After the husking was over, everyone ate supper. The food was piled on a table made of two planks placed side by side.

Slowly Eli walked along the table, hunting for food that he thought would taste best. When he found the crock of beans, the cheese, and the bread and butter his mother had brought, he stopped to take some.

Eli put two pickled pears on his platter. Then he noticed that someone back of him took two pickled pears also.

"Please excuse me," said the boy's voice, "but I wanted to get some of those good pickles. I like pickles, don't you?"

Eli turned and saw the boy he had kissed. When the boy grinned, he showed that he had lost two front teeth.

"I don't like you," said Eli, starting to walk away from the boy.

"Why don't you like me?" asked the boy. "I didn't tell you to kiss me."

The boy followed Eli and sat down on a bench beside him. "My name is Mose Hartley," he said. "What is your name?"

"Eli Whitney," answered Eli coldly.

"We just moved to Westboro last month," said Mose. "Are you new around here?"

Eli shook his head. Somehow he just couldn't be nice to the boy.

"Want to see something?" asked Mose, taking a big bite of pickled pear.

"No!" answered Eli.

Mose simply shrugged his shoulders and took something from his pocket.

Eli looked, but he didn't want to let on that he was interested. Then, suddenly, with a flick of his finger, Mose flipped a large blade from a jackknife. Eli sat up and stared! He had never seen a jackknife before.

"Like to whittle?" asked Mose.

By now Eli was beginning to feel better about Mose. Possibly he wasn't so bad after all.

Eli drew a whistle from his pocket. He had whittled the whistle from a twig, and shaped it like a bird. He put the whistle to his mouth and blew a shrill blast.

"Whew, that's a fine whistle," said Mose. "May I blow it?"

"May I see your knife?" asked Eli, handing the whistle to Mose.

Eli examined the knife closely. He flipped the blade open and shut. He ran his finger along the blade, and found it sharper than anything he had ever seen before.

Finally Eli handed the knife back to Mose. How he wished that he had one, too.

An hour later, Eli started to climb in the carriage to go home. Suddenly he saw something that looked like a jackknife lying on the ground. He stooped to pick it up, and sure enough it was a jackknife.

Eli looked at the jackknife. His thoughts spun round and round. Did the jackknife belong to Mose, or to someone else? It surely looked just like Mose's jackknife.

For a moment Eli slipped the jackknife into his pocket. He liked the way it felt in his pocket. If only he could keep it, he would be the happiest boy in the world.

"Is everyone ready to go?" asked Mr. Whitney, beside the carriage.

"No!" cried Eli. "I just found a jackknife here on the ground. I think it belongs to Mose Hartley, and I want to return it."

Eli ran back to the Burkett house to look for Mose but couldn't find him. Mose had already gone home.

"Well, tomorrow I'll make a special trip over to Mose's house to return the jackknife," said Eli. "He will be very sad when he finds out that he has lost it."

It was clear and cold and the stars shone brightly overhead. *"Poor Richard's Almanack* was right about the weather tonight," said Mr. Whitney. "I think that I'll keep the *Almanack* around for a while."

"Yes, it looks as if the *Almanack* is about as safe as I am in predicting weather," said Richard, with a smile.

Eli and Mose

WHEN ELI awakened the next morning, he felt strangely excited about something. He slipped one hand under his pillow to see whether the jackknife was still there. He had put it there when he went to bed to make certain that it would be safe.

He stroked the jackknife lovingly. It was almost the finest thing that he had ever seen. How he wished that it was his!

"I must not think of keeping the jackknife," he said. "It belongs to someone else. I'm almost certain that it belongs to Mose, and I must find out today, if I can."

Eli planned to go to Mose's house sometime during the morning. He knew that Mose would be very unhappy without his knife.

Just now, he didn't know where Mose lived, but he would find out. Mose's house might be hard to find, because Mose had said that he was new to the neighborhood.

Then Eli had a new idea about the knife. He would use it to make something, before he tried to return it. He was sure that Mose wouldn't care if he used the knife.

"I will make a little boat with the knife," he thought. "Then I will sail the boat on the creek by our house."

With these thoughts in mind, he went down to breakfast. He would use the knife to make something before he returned it.

During breakfast he kept thinking about the boat. He planned in his mind the exact kind of boat that he wanted to make.

Eli knew that his father would not approve of his keeping the jackknife long enough to make something. Nor would his father want him to waste time making a boat.

He wondered whether his father had ever made any toys when he was a boy. Now his father seemed to think that everything anyone made should be useful.

At last he finished his morning chores and went to his father's shop. He looked for a piece of wood good for making the boat. Soon he found just the piece that he wanted.

He took the piece of wood to a bench just beneath a window. Then he took out the knife and began to whittle. In a few minutes his father came into the shop.

"I hope that you are making something useful," said Mr. Whitney. "You can't waste time whittling something we don't need. Always make something that we can use."

Eli's face turned red. He knew that his father wouldn't approve of his making a boat.

"Come now," said Mr. Whitney. "I want you to deliver four chairs to the Hartley family, that moved into our neighborhood last month."

"Oh, good," said Eli. "Now I can ask Mose about the jackknife."

Eli hurried into the house to get a jacket to wear on the trip. When he returned, his father helped him to mount a horse with two chairs tied on each side of the saddle. Then he rode away toward Mose's house.

MOSE, A HAPPY BOY

Clipity clop, clipity clop went the horse along the road. Eli began to think of what he would say to Mose about the knife. Would Mose think that he had found the knife, or would Mose think that he had stolen it?

60

Once more he wondered whether the jackknife really belonged to Mose. If it didn't belong to Mose, to whom did it belong?

"There was only one thing to do," Eli decided. He would show the knife to Mose and ask him whether it belonged to him. If it didn't, then he would have to look further.

He tried to think of something else besides the jackknife. "Winter will soon be here," he said to himself. "Then we'll spend long winter evenings sitting before the fireplace. If I only had a jackknife, I could whittle while we sit before the fireplace."

Several times Eli tried to think of things besides the jackknife. Each time, however, he wound up thinking of it again.

Shortly Eli reached the Hartley farm. He turned the horse into a lane and rode toward the house. Mose saw him coming and ran out to meet him. "Oh, hello, Eli," he shouted.

"Hello, Mose," cried Eli. "Did you lose your jackknife last night at the husking bee?"

"Yes, I did," answered Mose, "but how did you know that I lost it?"

"Because I found a jackknife last night that looked exactly like yours," said Eli, pulling the knife from his pocket.

"Oh, thank you!" cried Mose, taking the jack-knife and caressing it fondly. "I was afraid that I would never see it again. Now I can go ahead with my carving. Come in and let me show you what I am making."

Just then Eli happened to think about the chairs. "Is your father at home?" he asked. "He ordered some chairs from my father, and I have brought them to him."

"Yes, he is here," answered Mose. "I'll run into the house to get him, then he'll help you dismount. You can't get off very well with all those chairs around you."

Mr. Hartley came out and untied the chairs so that Eli could dismount. "These are fine chairs," he said, looking them over. "Your father certainly is a good worker."

"Yes," said Eli, "he wants everything that he makes to be good. Someday I hope to help him make chairs in his shop."

Mose led the way into the house and showed Eli a large wooden spoon that he was making for his mother. "The spoon is about half done," he said. "Now that you found my knife, I'll soon finish whittling the spoon."

"How will your mother use the spoon?" asked Eli, noticing how big it was.

"She'll use it for stirring things in kettles when she is cooking," said Mose. "It will be a cooking spoon."

"Will it be a surprise?" asked Eli.

"No, Mother asked me to make it for her," answered Mose. "She knows about it."

"Well, I want to see the spoon after you finish it," said Eli. "Then perhaps sometime I can make a spoon for my mother. I have an old knife now, but one of these days I hope to get a good knife like yours."

The boys talked a few minutes longer, and Eli rose to leave. "I must start back," he said, "so my parents won't be worried about me. I promised them that I would come right back after I delivered the chairs."

"Thank you again for returning my jackknife," said Mose. "I don't know what I would have done without it."

"I'm glad that I found it," said Eli. "Last night after I kissed you, I almost hated you. Then when you showed me your knife, I began to like you. Now, I like you real well."

"I like you, too," said Mose, "and I'm glad that you kissed me. If you hadn't kissed me, I might not have known you."

64

Eli went back to his horse. "I'm glad that you moved into our neighborhood," he called to Mose. "Bring your jackknife and come over to see me sometime. Maybe I'll have a knife, and we can whittle together."

Eli let the horse walk all the way home. He wanted to have plenty of time to think along the way. He wanted to think of ways in which he could get a jackknife.

Should he ask his father to get him a jackknife? Mr. Whitney was a kind father, but he thought that boys always should work. He wouldn't want Eli to waste his time whittling. Besides, he would think that Eli's old homemade knife was good enough. Eli decided not to ask his father for a jackknife.

Could he ask his mother? He could ask her, but she hadn't any money. She didn't have money to buy things for herself. She couldn't get him a knife, even if she wanted to.

Then Eli began to think of ways in which he might earn money himself. Could he work on one of the neighbors' farms? Could he make something to sell?

The first thing he knew, he was home!

THE PEDDLER COMES

Some days later the sound of a horn came, sweet and clear, to everyone on the Whitney farm. Everyone on the farm was excited.

Mr. Whitney and Eli left the shop where they were working, and hurried to the house. Mrs. Whitney and Betsey hurried down from the attic. Josiah left his play. All gathered outside the kitchen door next to the lane.

Richard came up a few minutes later. "Is something wrong?" he asked anxiously.

"Oh, no," said Mrs. Whitney, "Amby, the peddler, is coming. That's all."

"I have a few yards of linen to trade for some ribbons!" said Betsey happily.

"What good are ribbons?" teased Eli. "All you can do with ribbons is put them on your dresses and in your hair."

Betsey turned to Eli. "What are you going to get from Amby?"

"Nothing," answered Eli. "I haven't anything to trade with him. Besides, he doesn't have anything that I want."

"Amby is coming!" cried Josiah.

Soon Amby Benedict arrived, carrying grips on his back as usual. He was a jolly half-Indian who had been coming to farmhouses around Westboro for twenty years.

"How do," smiled Andy, letting go of the straps that held the two grips on his back. "I have lots of nice things to show you."

He opened his grips, and everyone gathered around to see what he had inside.

68

Mr. Whitney complained of aching shoulder muscles. He knew that Amby would have a remedy. Amby was famous for his medicines.

"You need my crawling plasters," cried Amby. "They follow the pain and when they catch it—*whoosh*." With a flick of his brown hand across his throat he showed what the plasters would do to the pain.

Mr. Whitney traded a piece of leather for several of Amby's wonderful plasters. Mrs. Whitney traded some homespun cloth for special dyes and spices. Betsey traded some linen cloth for ribbons and hard candy.

Amby looked at Eli. "I guess I don't want anything this time," said Eli.

"Come and look anyway," said Amby. "It won't cost you anything to look."

Mrs. Whitney brought Amby some bread and butter and a jug of milk. While Amby ate and drank, Eli looked inside the grips.

There were bottles of medicines and salves and plasters. There were inks and pans and pots and cooky cutters. There were spices and dyes and ribbons and marbles and candy.

Suddenly Eli came across six shining jack-knives mounted on a board. The jackknives were beautiful, and he would give almost anything to have one. He blinked and blinked.

All the while Amby was watching. He took a big drink of milk and waved toward the knives. "Look them over, Eli," he said. "Maybe you'll think of something to trade."

Eli looked over the jackknives carefully, but could think of nothing to trade!

"The jackknives are pretty nice, eh?" smiled Amby. "You like a nice jackknife for yourself, but you have nothing to trade? There must be something around here to trade."

Eli looked around thoughtfully. No one helped him to think of anything to trade.

Amby's eyes strayed toward the Indian broom that stood by the kitchen door. His eyes gleamed. "You make broom?"

"Yes," replied Eli.

Amby went over and examined it. "Fine broom, very fine broom," he said. "Very nice smooth handle on broom.

"You want knife," Amby continued. "If you will have twelve brooms ready for Amby when he comes back, he will give you knife."

"You will?" cried Eli. "Oh, I could hug you for being so good to me."

Amby backed away. "Nah, nah!" he grinned. "That's girl stuff."

Eli raced back to the shop. "Soon," he shouted, "I'll have a jackknife."

Eli's School Days

ONE MORNING Mr. Whitney was making a chair, and Eli was working on a broom. Soon, Mr. Whitney finished his chair and looked at Eli as if he had something on his mind.

He noticed how much Eli had grown recently. Already he was becoming a big boy, big enough to go to school.

"What are you thinking about, Father?" asked Eli. "You seem to be worried about something. What is the trouble?"

"The trouble is you, Eli," replied Mr. Whitney. "You are becoming a big boy, and you must go to school this year."

72

Mr. Whitney picked up another piece of wood, and began to work on another chair.

"I don't want to go to school," said Eli.

"You have to go," said Mr. Whitney. "You have to learn to read and write and cipher."

"I don't want to learn to read and write and cipher," said Eli stubbornly. "I want to learn to run the lathe."

Mr. Whitney laid a kindly hand on his son's shoulder. "I know that you love the shop, and that you are very good with tools. Someday you will make a fine mechanic, but being a mechanic will not be enough.

"You will need to know how to read and write and cipher. You can't learn to do these things, unless you go to school."

Eli sighed. He knew that he would have to go, but he hated to think of staying all day in a stuffy schoolroom! He hated to think of a stern school-master watching over him!

Mr. Whitney left the shop. Eli wandered over to the window and looked out over the rolling hills on the Whitney farm.

He clenched one hand. "I don't want to go to school. I don't, I don't, I don't!"

Mrs. Whitney came to the door. "Don't worry, Eli," she said, trying to soothe him. "You will soon get used to going to school."

"How do you know?" asked Eli.

"Oh, I went to school once myself," said Mrs. Whitney. "Besides, Betsey will be going to school with you. You won't be lonesome."

"I know my letters already," said Eli proudly.

"Yes, you learn quickly," said his mother.

"I still don't want to go to school!" said Eli again, almost starting to cry. "I want to stay at home and work in the shop. I can learn more here than I can at school."

"You heard what your father said, and you must obey," said Mrs. Whitney calmly.

74

"I heard all right, but I still don't want to go," said Eli.

"Well, Betsey will need you," said Mrs. Whitney. "You can help to look after her."

Eli hadn't thought about helping Betsey. "That's different," he said. "If I can be of any help to Betsey, I'll go."

"Thank you, Eli," said Mrs. Whitney. "You are a good brother to Betsey."

GLOOMY DAYS

The first day of school soon came. Eli and Betsey followed the path that led to the little frame schoolhouse. It was about a mile and a half from the Whitney farm.

"I wish that I were as old as Richard," Eli said sadly along the way. "Then I could stay at home and help with the butchering."

Under one arm he carried a book called the

New England Primer, and in one hand he carried a small basket full of lunch.

"Here we are!" cried Betsey.

At the sight of the schoolhouse Eli's heart grew heavier than ever. When he looked inside the doorway, he felt that he could go no further. Everything looked old and musty.

Eli caught a glimpse of Master Nathaniel Phipps, a skinny, scowling old man with a long nose. He was seated at a small desk in the middle of the room.

Master Phipps looked at Eli sharply. "What is your name?" he asked.

"Eli Whitney," whispered Eli.

"Take your seat," said Master Phipps, waving Eli to a bench with his long bony arm.

Eli went to the side of the room and sat down with several boys and girls of his own age. He looked around for Mose, but could not find him. How he wished that Mose were there!

Like the other children, Eli folded his arms and stared straight ahead. He tried to do exactly what the other children did.

There were benches on three sides of the room. A fireplace filled the fourth side. In the center of the room there was a small platform where the schoolmaster had his desk. He sat at his desk on top of the platform.

The schoolmaster's back was toward the fireplace. All the pupils sat in front or at the sides where he could see them.

It was difficult for Eli to sit still. The bench was hard and his feet didn't quite touch the floor. By and by he started to squirm and wriggle. Before long Master Phipps looked over in that direction and saw him.

"Eli Whitney, come here!" he called.

Eli got up and went.

"Hold out your hand, palm up!"

Eli held out his hand.

Smack! Master Phipps's ruler came down on Eli's open palm.

"Now go back to your seat!" he ordered, glaring around the schoolroom. "Let that be an example to all of you who want to squirm and wriggle in your seats."

Eli went back to his seat. "I hate school!" he thought. "I knew that I would!"

A few minutes later, Eli heard the master call his name again.

"Do you know your letters?" demanded the master in a cold tone of voice.

"Yes, sir, I do," replied Eli.

"Then repeat them," said the master.

"A, B, C, D . . . er—ah, F . . ." Frantically Eli looked around. Then he saw Betsey's anxious face and took heart. "G, H, I, J." He went on through the alphabet.

"Fairly good," said Master Phipps. "You may sit with the pupils learning to spell."

Eli moved to join a group of slightly older children. He looked at the bench on the other side of the room. This was the bench where the older pupils sat.

The bench was empty today. There usually was work at home for the older boys and girls. Only on days when there was no work, and on rainy days, were they allowed to come to school. How Eli envied them!

Eli opened his primer. He knew the letters, but he couldn't read the words.

Master Phipps told him to learn to spell the words, but didn't tell him what the words were. Eli sat quietly, whispering the letters over and over again to himself.

Suddenly Master Phipps announced: "Let us study our spelling lesson together."

Everyone, except Eli and the other new scholars, knew what Master Phipps meant. He meant that they would have loud school.

Seventeen children's voices began chanting, "L-a, l-a, d-y, d-y, lady; s-h-a, s-h-a, d-y, d-y, shady; l-i, l-i, v-e, v-e, live; g-i, g-i, v-e, v-e, give." And so on and on.

Then, after what seemed a long, long time, the master called, "Noon recess."

There was a wild scramble for lunches and wraps. Soon the schoolhouse was empty. All the children wanted to go outdoors.

They ate their lunches quickly. Then the boys played ball, ran races, and wrestled. The girls played hopscotch, ring-around-a-rosy, and London Bridge. All too soon Master Phipps called again. This time he said, "Books!"

The afternoon was just like the morning. Finally, Eli and Betsey started home. "I hate school!" said Eli. "I'd much rather stay at home. I'd learn something there."

"Didn't you learn anything at school today?" asked Betsey, trying to make fun.

"Oh, yes," said Eli, starting to laugh. "L-a, l-a, d-y, d-y, lady; s-h-a, s-h-a, d-y, d-y, shady; l-i, l-i, v-e, v-e, live; g-i, g-i, v-e, v-e, give!"

A NEW PUPIL AT SCHOOL

"Did you have trouble keeping a good fire under the kettle when you were butchering to-day, Father?" asked Eli that evening.

"No, Eli," replied Mr. Whitney. "Why?"

"Well, I thought if you did, I could stay at home tomorrow and tend it for you."

Mr. Whitney laughed. "It will take a better excuse than that, Eli, to keep you out of school tomorrow," he said.

Before Eli went to bed, he took a candle and went out to the shop. He looked over his finished brooms. There were only six, but he needed twelve to get a jackknife!

"How can I make six more brooms before

Amby comes again?" he thought. "Now I'll have to spend most of my time in school."

Amby might come any day now. This trip would be the last one he would make through the countryside until spring.

"A penny for your thoughts," teased Betsey, on the way to school the next day.

"School, school!" growled Eli. "Why do I have to go to school when I could be making brooms and earning my jackknife?"

"Shh! There's the schoolmaster right ahead of us," warned Betsey.

Sure enough. There was Master Phipps walking along ahead of them with his head bowed and his hands clasped behind his back. Eli didn't say another word on the way.

When Eli reached school, he was happy to find Mose Hartley in the room. Now he might come to like school a little better.

Eli ran to join Mose at recess. Together they

started for a tiny wooded ravine that Eli had discovered the day before.

"How are the brooms coming?" asked Mose. "How many have you finished?"

"I've finished six," replied Eli.

"Will you have twelve finished when Amby comes again?" asked Mose.

"Not if I come to school," said Eli.

"Don't you work on them after you've finished your chores at night?" asked Mose.

"No, I don't," replied Eli.

"You'll be surprised to see how much you can get done in an evening," said Mose.

"That's a good idea," said Eli.

Mose scratched his head thoughtfully. "Why don't you bring a broom to work on during the noon hour?" he asked.

Eli thought of what his father had once told him. "If you really want something, you can always find a way of getting it."

Yes, his father was right. If he really wanted something, he could find a way of getting it. There was only one thing to do. He must finish the brooms for Amby, even though he had to go to school every day.

"I'll bring a sapling to school tomorrow," he said to Mose. "Then we can come here at noon, so that I can work on it."

"Good," said Mose. "Now I'm sure that you'll have the brooms for Amby."

Happier Days for Eli

THAT AFTERNOON Eli went straight home from school. Eli finished his chores quickly and hurried to the shop. His brooms and saplings were stacked in one corner.

He took out his knife and set to work. "I'll work hard," he vowed. "I must have twelve brooms finished for Amby."

He cut a ring around the sapling, one foot and two inches from the big end. Below the ring he carefully took off the bark. Then, he began slivering the barked part of the sapling all the way up to the ring.

"It takes a lot of slivering to make a broom

out of a sapling," he thought as he started the broom. "The slivers have to be just right, not too big and not too little."

Eli was working busily when Betsey called him to supper. He wanted to get a good start on the broom that evening, if he could.

"Is that the sapling you'll take to school to-morrow?" she asked.

"No, I'm going to work on this one at home. I'll take a fresh sapling to school."

After supper he worked a little longer on the broom. He was surprised to find how much he could do in a short time.

The next day, when he left for school, he carried, besides his primer and lunch, a sapling and his old knife.

Mose met him at the door of the schoolhouse. "I see you have your sapling," he said.

"Yes, I have it," replied Eli, "but where can I put it until the noon recess?"

"How about putting it in our secret spot in the ravine?" asked Mose.

"That's a fine idea," said Eli. The two boys ran to the ravine, and slipped the sapling under some big drooping bushes.

Noon recess was slow coming, but when it came, Mose and Eli hurried to the hollow. First they sat down on a log and ate their lunches. Then Eli took out his knife and started to work on his broom. Mose pulled out his jackknife and began whittling, too.

"What are you making, Mose?" asked Eli.

"Heel pegs," replied Mose. "The cobbler in Westboro pays me two cents apiece for them. I can earn good money making pegs."

Both boys worked on until Master Phipps called, "Books!" Eli was pleased with the progress he had made. He had finished slivering the large end of the sapling.

He flipped back the slivers and examined

them carefully to make sure he had done everything right. Then he slipped the broom carefully
back under the bushes. "Tomorrow," he said,
"I'll make the handle for the broom."

"While you do that, I'll whittle more heel
pegs," grinned Mose.

That evening after school Eli worked on a
broom at home. During the noon hour the next
day he worked on the broom at school.

When the boys reached the ravine, Eli began
to make the handle of the broom. This time he
worked on the top end of the sapling.

He kept slivering until the top end was small
enough for a handle. Then he took a piece of
hard-twisted string and tied the slivers down.
Last he trimmed them off even.

Master Phipps called, "Books!" The boys hurried back to school.

"I can finish the broom handle tomorrow,"
said Eli happily along the way.

"It looks finished already," said Mose.

"Oh, no," said Eli. "I have to scrape it with a piece of glass to make it smooth. Then I have to bore a hole in the end."

"What for?" asked Eli.

"For putting in a loop of leather," said Eli. "I always put loops on my broom handles, so that the brooms can be hung on pegs."

"No wonder Amby liked your brooms so well," said Mose. "They will bring good prices in the towns he visits."

"They'll bring me a new jackknife!"

By the end of the week Eli had two brooms finished, ready to store away. "Now I have only four more to make," he said.

THE MISSING BROOM

Two weeks passed.

Eli felt very gay as he hurried home from

school. He had reasons to be gay. He was working on his last two brooms and would have them finished in time for Amby's next trip.

Mr. Allen, who lived down the road, was in Mr. Whitney's shop. "I hear that Amby is on his way to our neighborhood," he said. "He should reach here in a couple of days."

Mr. Whitney nodded. "Amby is as regular as sunup and sundown, and he always has been. He can't come too soon to suit me. I need more of his famous crawling plasters."

Eli's heart pounded. Within two short days, he would have his jackknife. Already he could feel the smooth metal in his hand as if he were whittling something.

For a long time he had wanted a water wheel! Now he could make one. He and Mose could put it on the creek together.

While Mr. Whitney and Mr. Allen went on talking, Eli finished a broom. He tied the leather loop in the handle. Now he had only one more broom to finish, and he would finish that at school tomorrow.

That night Eli went to bed happy. The next day at school he finished the broom as he had planned. "I won't tell Mose about Amby coming," he said. "It will be more fun to show him my knife as a surprise."

That afternoon he raced out of the schoolhouse and started to run home. Then he came to a stop. How silly he felt! He had come away without bringing his broom!

"I guess I'm just excited," he said, whirling around. He ran back to the schoolhouse, and on into the secret hollow. Then he reached under the brushes to get his broom. Alas! The broom was gone! It wasn't there!

He searched everywhere, but he could not find the broom. Finally he sat down on the dry leaves and bit his lips to keep from crying. He knew that he could never finish another broom before Amby came. Now he would have to wait until spring before he could get a knife.

Where could the broom be? Someone must have taken it from its hiding place. Could Mose have taken it? Surely not, but he was the only one who knew where it was hidden!

The next morning Eli could hardly wait for the time to come to go to school. He wanted to be sure that the broom was gone.

He searched again, but found no sign of the broom. Then he began to wonder how he should treat Mose, if he was a thief.

The morning passed and Mose did not come to school. During the noon recess, Eli went to the hollow where he could be by himself.

When he reached the hollow, he sat down on a log to think. All sorts of things went through his mind. By and by he heard a low clear whistle, and he knew that Mose was coming.

Eli turned and looked. There he saw Mose coming with the missing broom!

Eli was speechless.

Mose slid down to sit by him. "Here's your broom, Eli," he said. "I took it home with me last night to show to Father and Mother. I had some special chores to do this morning and couldn't bring it back."

"Oh, that's all right," said Eli, beginning to feel better. "What did your parents think of the broom?"

"They thought it was fine," said Mose, "and so did Mr. Jenkins, the storekeeper. He'll pay you six cents apiece to make a dozen brooms to sell in his store."

Eli could hardly believe the words. He could earn seventy-two cents making brooms! Why that didn't seem possible! With his new knife, making twelve brooms would be easy.

Mose was no thief after all!

That evening Eli hurried home with the broom to tell his parents the good news. When he entered the kitchen, his mother said, "Amby was just here. He wanted to see you, and you can easily overtake him on horseback."

A few seconds later Eli climbed on a horse with his brooms and started down the road. He couldn't make the horse go fast, because the brooms were hard to hold. They slipped this way and that way, sometimes cracking his ankles and sometimes smacking the horse's sides.

"I hope Amby hasn't gone very far," thought Eli, trying to hold on to the brooms.

Fortunately Eli didn't have to go far. Soon he saw Amby trudging down the road ahead with his grips strapped on his back.

"Amby! Amby!" he called, bringing his horse to a stop. "Here are your brooms. I have come to get my knife."

"I was expecting you," said Amby, swinging his grips from his shoulders. He opened one of the grips and handed Eli a jackknife. Then he swung the twelve brooms on his back with his grips, and started on down the road.

Eli could hardly wait to get home to show the new jackknife to his parents and Betsey. He made the horse gallop all the way along the road and up the lane. He slid off the horse and rushed into the kitchen. "Look, here is my new jackknife!" he called.

Eli reached in his pocket to pull out his knife, but the knife was gone!

"My knife is gone!" he cried. "It must have slipped out of my pocket!"

Eli rushed from the kitchen back to the horse. "Where are you going?" called his mother.

"I'm going to look for my knife!" answered Eli, starting to climb on the horse.

"Oh, no!" called Mrs. Whitney. "It's too dark

tonight. You'll have to wait until morning to look for your knife."

Then Eli began to wonder about the knife. Where had he lost it? How could it have possibly slipped from his pocket?

"I'll search every inch of that road tomorrow," he said. "I'll find that knife somehow, even if I have to look all day."

Fortunately the next day was Saturday and there was no school. Almost before daylight Eli started out on foot to look for the knife. He looked to the left and to the right, and hours later came to the spot where he had met Amby. Not a trace of the knife had he found.

He sat down beside the road to think and to rest. Soon he looked up and saw Mose coming. "What's the matter?" asked Mose.

"I've lost my new jackknife," said Eli.

Mose jammed his hand into his pocket and drew out a new shiny jackknife. "Is that your jackknife?" he asked, holding it out on the palm of his hand.

"Yes, it is, but where did you find it?" asked Eli. "Where did I lose it?"

"Down the road," answered Mose. "I found it this morning when I came down the road to get one of our cows. There it lay right in the middle of the road."

Eli was too happy to speak. He just stood looking fondly at his knife.

Mose laughed. "I guess we'd better tie our jackknives around our necks," he said. "One of these times one of us will lose a knife and the other won't be around to find it."

Wintertime

HALF BURIED beneath a pile of his mother's warm quilts, Eli woke up and shivered. The air in his bedroom was frosty. He snuggled down further under the quilts.

"Even though today's my birthday," he thought, "I don't want to get up."

Just then Mr. Whitney called, "Eli, Eli! It's time for you to get up."

Eli took a deep breath, and leaped bravely out of bed. Stepping on the cold floor was like stepping on a cake of ice. He drew on his clothes and made a wild dash for the kitchen. The kitchen was the only warm room in the house,

100

and this room wasn't really warm. The only warm place was a spot in front of the fireplace.

Eli splashed icy water from the wooden basin on his face, and stood in front of the crackling fire. Then, after he became toasted on both sides, he sat down to breakfast.

Richard came in a few moments later and stood in front of the fireplace. "It's going to snow today," he said, rubbing his hands together before the burning logs. "I wouldn't be surprised to see a blizzard come our way."

Mrs. Whitney laughed. "You amuse me with your weather predictions, Richard," she said. She took down *Poor Richard's Almanack* to see what it said about the weather.

"December the sixth . . . hm," she began. "Well, for once you and *Poor Richard's Almanack* agree." She looked at Betsey and Eli. "You children won't have to go to school today. I wouldn't want you to get lost in a snowstorm."

"Ah!" thought Eli. "This is the kind of weather for me. No school today!"

Everybody worked hard that day. Wood for the fire was brought in. All the buckets and jugs were filled with water. The animals were fed, and bedded down with plenty of straw. Corn was brought down from the attic. Food was brought up from the cellar.

It was late afternoon before the family settled down by the fireplace. Everyone was grateful to be warm and snug. Outside, rain and sleet fell. It would be a long, hard storm.

Everyone had been too busy during the day to mention Eli's birthday. When Mrs. Whitney and Betsey set the table for supper, however, Eli found that it hadn't been forgotten.

Mrs. Whitney got out her best white linen tablecloth and her best silver and pewter dishes. In the center of the table she placed a big bowl of stew, made of beef and carrots and parsnips and potatoes. The stew had been simmering all day in the big iron kettle in the fireplace. There was plenty of fresh bread and butter to eat with the stew.

The meal was gay and jolly. When it was over, Mrs. Whitney brought out a small fruitcake. She almost never baked a cake.

"Mmm," said Eli and Betsey.

"This is your favorite kind of cake, Eli," Mrs. Whitney said, cutting the cake into small slices. "I put in plenty of nuts and currants, and I sprinkled sugar all over the top."

After everyone had finished the cake, Mr. Whitney said, "Eli, will you please go upstairs to get my tobacco?"

"Yes, sir," said Eli. He offered no objection to going to the icy-cold upstairs, because he knew why he was being sent.

When he returned, he found many wonderful birthday gifts stacked up on the table—a tin lunch bucket from his father, a top from Josiah, and a pair of stockings from Betsey. There was a leather knife case for his belt from Richard. There were two red-and-white checked linen shirts from his mother!

"What a lucky boy I am!" cried Eli.

BY THE FIRESIDE

Eli, Betsey, and Mrs. Whitney made short work of clearing the table. They were eager to get closer to the fire.

Mr. Whitney came in. "Snow will be drifted high by morning," he said.

Eli kept his gifts close beside him. He looked them over carefully, one by one.

He held up the stockings where everyone could see them. "These will come in handy this winter when I go out in the deep snow," he laughed. Then he picked up the linen shirts.

He smoothed the folds of the shirts. How soft and smooth the linen felt! After that, tow felt as prickly as a porcupine's back!

"What a pity," he said, "that linen is the only cloth for summer clothes."

"There are other light stuffs," said his father. "There are silks and satins and such, but they are much too expensive for common use. They are not sturdy enough, anyway.

"I've heard," Mr. Whitney went on, "that people are making a strong, light cloth from the fibers of cotton plants. People in the Southern colonies are already wearing it."

"Then why don't we plant cotton and spin and weave cotton cloth?" asked Eli.

Mr. Whitney laughed. "There are several reasons, Eli. First, cotton plants would not grow well in our climate. Second, it is quite a task to get cotton fibers ready for spinning and weaving in making the cloth.

"You see, cotton fibers aren't like linen fibers, that we get from stalks of flax plants. Strangely, cotton fibers come from the flowers of cotton plants. After the flowers wither, they leave growths or pods, called bolls."

Eli was listening with interest. Mr. Whitney smiled and went on. "This pod dries and breaks open. Inside is the white fluffy cotton fiber, but alas, there are seeds in the cotton. The seeds are small and as hard to remove as cockleburs. It is a pity, for without the seeds, cotton fibers could easily be spun and woven."

"Why can't the seeds be taken out?" asked Eli.

"They can be, but only by hand, one by one. I don't believe that cotton fibers ever will be used for making cloth."

Eli sighed. He guessed boys would always be uncomfortable in prickly shirts.

He yawned. Then he shivered.

"I'll warm your sheets tonight, Eli," said his

mother, noting that he was cold. "Hand me the bed warmer so that I may heat it."

Mrs. Whitney filled the covered skillet-like pan with hot coals. When she swished the pan back and forth between the icy bed sheets, it warmed them quickly. While she was upstairs, Eli watched his father wind his watch. "May I hold it, Father?" he asked. He took it and held it to his ear. "I wonder what makes it tick."

"You'd better take your watch back to Boston, Mr. Whitney," laughed Richard, "or Eli will try to find out."

Mr. Whitney took his watch and put it back in his pocket.

"Good night," said Eli. "Thanks for a wonderful birthday." He was soon fast asleep between his warm sheets.

New Adventures

A FEW YEARS LATER, in the spring of 1777, Eli was a strong, sturdy lad of eleven. One morning he was in the shop. He stood before the turning lathe. He was making chair legs.

The whir of the lathe mingled with the songs of the birds outside. Eli hummed a gay tune, too. It was spring. School was out. He was doing what he liked better than anything in the world. He was happy.

During the last four years he had learned many things in his father's shop. He had learned to run the lathe. There was no end to the fine things he could turn out on it. He could whittle

108

better than any boy for miles around. His wonderful jackknife was always busy. It was still his favorite possession.

Eli grinned as he remembered his father's surprise when he had shown him the first nails he had made.

"As good nails as any blacksmith can make," Mr. Whitney had said.

Eli sniffed the sweet scent of his mother's flower garden, outside the shop window. He listened to a wren. Many birds lived in the birdhouses he had hung from the branches. Eli was proud of those birdhouses.

There were round birdhouses and square ones and short ones and tall ones. Some had chimneys and porches like real houses. The birds liked all the houses.

Eli was thinking about Richard. "I wonder what he will do, when his redemption term is up?" Then he worried. "I hope he doesn't leave

Westboro. I hope he doesn't move so far away that I can't see him often."

He had heard his father say, "I am going to give Richard ten acres of land, a plow, a horse and a few household things. Those gifts should help him get started."

The Whitneys had grown very fond of Richard. He seemed to Eli like an older brother.

Mr. Whitney entered the shop. "I have an errand for you, Eli. Your mother is almost out of corn meal. You must take some corn to the gristmill and have it ground."

Eli quickly made ready to go. He liked to make trips to Westboro. There were so many things to do and to see there.

Mr. Whitney threw two sacks of corn across the back of the horse. Eli climbed up.

His mother appeared in the doorway. "Here is a length of linen, Eli." She handed him a small parcel. "Take the linen to the dish turner's and trade it for a dozen pewter spoons. Good-by, and be careful on the way."

"I will, Mother." Eli slipped the parcel into his saddlebag.

Spring rains had made the road a sticky mass of mud. *Slurp, slurp, slurp,* went the horse's hoofs. "We'll be splattered all over by the time we get to Westboro," Eli said to the horse. He patted the horse on its neck.

He was right. When they drew up before the gristmill, they both were muddy, but neither seemed to mind very much.

The miller, Mr. Vaughn, was a jolly good fellow. "Certainly I'll grind your corn," he boomed, "but you'll have to wait a spell. There are several customers ahead of you."

"That's all right," said Eli. "I am in no hurry."

"Most boys your age are in no hurry when they come to Westboro," chuckled Mr. Vaughn. He carried the sacks of corn into the mill. Eli tied

111

his horse to a fence beside the mill and started to walk around the village. He was really glad for the opportunity.

THE BLACKSMITH SHOP

Eli knew just where he wanted to go and what he wanted to see. He started down the muddy main street of the village.

He first stopped at the bakeshop to get something to eat. "Give me a penny's worth of rolls," he said to the owner, "and please put them into a small bag."

A few seconds later Eli went on down the street, eating his rolls. He headed for Jed Hawkins' blacksmith shop.

When Eli came to the blacksmith shop, he peeked inside and saw Mr. Hawkins shoeing a horse. He was holding up one of the horse's front hoofs and nailing a shoe on the hoof.

112

Eli stepped quietly into the building and watched the blacksmith work for a moment. Mr. Hawkins began to shape another shoe for the horse. He heated it and made it red hot and hammered it to make it just the right shape. Then he placed it into a tub of water to cool it.

Next Mr. Hawkins picked up another of the horse's hoofs. He held the shoe to the horse's foot. Then he took a sharp knife and trimmed the hoof to make it fit the shoe.

Suddenly the blacksmith noticed Eli. "How are you?" he said. "What brings you to town?"

"I brought some corn to be ground at the mill," answered Eli.

"While you're waiting I guess you are looking around," said Mr. Hawkins.

"That's a fine thing to do," said the owner of the horse, who was seated on a bench.

"Yes, you can learn many things by looking," said Mr. Hawkins, putting on the last shoe.

114

The man on the bench paid the blacksmith, took his horse, and left the shop.

Mr. Hawkins picked up one of two slender pieces of iron that lay on the workbench. He heated it in the forge and placed it, red-hot, on the anvil. Then he began shaping it into graceful curves with his hammer.

"What is that going to be, Mr. Hawkins?" asked Eli curiously.

Mr. Hawkins started working on the other piece of metal. He curved it exactly as he had curved the first.

"These two pieces, put together," he said, "will become a pair of tiny tongs. With these tongs a man may pick a live coal from the fire, drop it into his pipe, and light his tobacco. A pipe-lighter, it is called. A gentleman saw one in Boston and asked me to make one for him."

"I think I'll try to make one," said Eli. "My father would like it." He got up from the bench.

"You have other shops to visit, I take it?"

"Yes, I have, sir," answered Eli. "And not much time to spend. Thank you for letting me stay here."

"You're welcome any time, my lad."

A short distance down the street, Eli stopped again. Piles of wooden staves, drying in the sun, told him this was a cooper's shop.

Mr. Cooper, for indeed that was his name, smiled at Eli. "Come in, boy," he said. "Come in and watch me make some wooden casks."

Eli saw wooden barrels, tubs, buckets, and casks of every size and shape stacked around the room. Mr. Cooper made fine products and had a good business.

Mr. Cooper showed Eli all of the products in his shop. He showed him how staves were made for the sides of the vessels and how the round ends were made. He showed him how iron bands were put on to hold the staves in place.

Eli spent a pleasant half-hour at Mr. Cooper's shop. He enjoyed seeing how the barrels, tubs, buckets, and casks were made.

Next Eli went to see Mr. Thompson, the wheelwright, who made and repaired wheels. "I'm glad that you came this week," said Mr. Thompson, "because next week I plan to make a trip to the country. I want to sell some of my wheels to the farmers."

Eli looked around the room. There were wheels of many sizes and shapes. "Do farmers use all these kinds of wheels?" asked Eli.

"Yes," replied Mr. Thompson. "Farmers are not very good at making wheels. They can make almost anything except wheels."

"I know," replied Eli. "Somehow farmers can't even make spinning wheels."

"Well, I'm glad that farmers can't make wheels," laughed Mr. Thompson. "If they could I would have to learn a new trade."

Eli talked with the wheelwright for a while, then went on to the dish turner's shop. He arrived just in time to see the dish turner making pewter spoons. He watched him pour the pewter mixture of tin and lead into a spoon mold. The mold was made of some kind of wood.

"What kind of wood is the mold made of, sir?" Eli asked Mr. Wheeler.

"Laurel wood," replied Mr. Wheeler. Soon he lifted the top of the mold and took out a fine pewter spoon. "Some people call laurel wood spoonwood, because it's especially good for making molds for spoons."

Eli saw how the mold was made. He looked at plates and mugs and platters and sugar bowls and dishes of every kind. They were made of silver and wood and pewter.

He was so interested that he forgot all about the linen his mother had given him. It was still in his saddlebag when, hours later, he threw the sacks of corn meal over the horse's back, mounted the horse, and started for home.

ELI, THE SPOONMAKER

When Eli reached home, he carried the sacks of meal into the kitchen. He was very happy about the things he had seen.

"Where are my spoons?" asked Mrs. Whitney. "Did you forget to get them?"

Eli's face turned red with shame. "Yes, Mother, I'm sorry," he said. "I forgot all about trading the linen for spoons."

"Well, I'll wager that you didn't forget to do certain things that you wanted to do," said his mother. "I'll wager that you didn't forget to stop at the blacksmith shop, the cooper's shop, and the wheelwright's shop."

"No, I didn't," said Eli. "I even went to the dish turner's shop, but forgot to get your spoons.

I promise to get them for you the very next time I go to town."

"I'm glad that I didn't ask you to buy me anything from Westboro," teased Betsey. "I know that you wouldn't have brought it."

The mention of spoons started Eli thinking. He wished that he could learn to make spoons in his father's shop. Making spoons would be simple, if he could get some old pewter dishes. All he would have to do would be to melt the dishes and pour the melted pewter into a mold. The mold would make the pewter the right shape for a new spoon.

"Have you any old pewter dishes that you don't want any longer?" Eli asked his mother.

"Yes, I have several old pewter dishes battered and worn, and I have some old pewter spoons," said his mother.

"May I have them?" asked Eli. "I want to melt them to make things."

"Well, you may have them, but please save one spoon," said his mother.

"What for?" asked Eli.

"To tie around your neck so that you'll remember to get my spoons the next time you go to Westboro," laughed his mother.

Betsey giggled and Eli grinned. He was glad that his mother was no longer angry. Somehow she never stayed angry very long.

The next day Eli started to make spoons. First he got two pieces of laurel wood, or spoonwood, and cut out places for molding the front and back of a spoon.

He scraped the two pieces smooth, so that they fit closely together. Then he fastened the pieces together with a hinge, so that he could open and close them.

Now he was ready to try the mold. He melted some of the old pewter dishes that his mother had given him. He poured the liquid pewter into the lower mold, and closed down the lid. Some of the liquid pewter oozed out. He had poured in more than the mold would hold.

"I will soon learn just how much pewter to pour in," he thought.

He waited for the pewter to harden. Then he lifted the top of the mold. There was a spoon, all right, but the liquid that had oozed out still clung to the edges.

Eli again poured pewter into the mold, not quite so much as he had the first time. The next spoon was perfect.

Betsey started to come into the shop. Eli quickly hid the spoon and the mold. "Supper is ready, Eli," she said.

Eli said nothing about spoons that evening, but he glowed inside. His idea had worked out even better than he had hoped.

He worked hard the next day. By afternoon he had poured the last of the melted old pewter.

In a shining row on the bench lay twenty-four new spoons!

Eli picked up all the spoons and walked quietly toward the kitchen. He peeked in the door. His mother was nowhere to be seen, so he laid the spoons in a row on the table. Then he tiptoed out of the room.

A few minutes later, his mother's cry of surprise came clear to the shop. Mrs. Whitney came hurrying out.

"You rapscallion!" she said. "So that is why you wanted the old pewter!"

Then she looked thoughtful. "Now what am I going to do with the linen?"

"I'll trade it for a pewter sugar bowl," said Eli, "and I won't forget the next time."

"No," said his mother, "I believe I have a better use for the linen."

Two days later, when Eli went to his room, he found something lying on his bed. He went over and looked at it. He could hardly believe his eyes. It was a brand-new, red-and-white checked linen shirt!

He ran down to the kitchen. "Oh, thank you, Mother, for the new shirt," he cried. "I like it very much."

"Well, I like my spoons very much, too," said his mother. Now I'm glad that you didn't get me the spoons in Westboro. These spoons are even better than you would have brought me from there."

Eli walked out of the house whistling. He whistled only when he was very happy.

What Makes
a Watch Tick?

ONE MORNING Mr. Allen rode into the yard. He
and Mr. Whitney were going into Westboro
together.

"Father will have his horse saddled in a moment," Eli said to Mr. Allen. "Won't you step
into the shop and wait?"

"I don't mind if I do, Eli," Mr. Allen replied,
swinging down from the saddle. "I always like
to look around the shop here."

He entered the shop and looked around. "Isn't
that a spoon mold up there, Eli?" He pointed to
the mold hanging from a peg.

"Yes, it is," replied Eli.

"I didn't know that you had one," said Mr. Allen. "I don't remember seeing it."

"I made it just a few days ago," replied Eli.

"That so? Hmm," Mr. Allen took it down and examined it. "I believe you could make some pretty fair spoons with this."

"Eli has made some fine spoons," said Mr. Whitney as he entered the shop. "Get one of your spoons and show it to Mr. Allen."

When Eli was out of hearing, Mr. Allen said, "That boy will never make a farmer. He is interested mostly in the workbench."

"Well," said Mr. Whitney, "he comes by his bent naturally. If he doesn't make a farmer, he will be a good mechanic. After all, mechanics are as necessary as farmers."

"I guess you're right," said Mr. Allen.

Eli came back with the spoon and Mr. Allen looked it over carefully.

"It's a fine spoon," he said. "My wife needs

126

some new ones. Monday is her birthday. Can you have a dozen ready by evening?"

"I have no more pewter," said Mr. Whitney.

"Well, I have some old platters at home which you can melt," said Mr. Allen. "Can your man Richard ride over and get the platters?"

"Yes, he can go, then Eli can make the spoons," said Mr. Whitney.

Richard rode away in one direction to get the old platters, and Mr. Whitney and Mr. Allen rode away in another direction.

Eli began to put some nails into a keg for a customer. He picked up the keg and happened to see his father's watch on the table, right where he was going to put the keg.

"Oh, my!" he said. "That was a narrow escape. I didn't know that the watch was there."

He picked up the watch and held it to his ear. He wished that he knew what made it tick. How he wanted to take it apart!

"No!" he told himself firmly, hanging the watch on a peg above the bench.

Richard soon returned to the shop, carrying several old pewter platters.

"Did you see Mr. Allen's beautiful daughter, Verity?" asked Eli.

Richard let out a long, happy sigh. "Yes, and she surely is beautiful," he said.

BUSY AFTERNOON

Eli set about melting the pewter. He began to pour the liquid into his spoon mold.

Each time he had to wait for the pewter to harden. While he waited he worked to straighten up the shop.

He bustled about the shop with a broom. Sawdust flew and so did shavings. He picked up tools and put them back on their pegs. He oiled the plane and filed a dull saw.

He passed the watch several times. Each time he was tempted to find out what made it tick, but he worked on.

Spoon after spoon was taken from the mold. Neater and neater grew the shop. Mr. Whitney's watch still hung on its peg. Eli took the eighth spoon from the mold. He looked at the watch. It was two o'clock. He could easily finish the spoons by evening.

He took the watch down. He held it to his ear: The tick-tick-tick was too much for him. Suddenly he opened up his knife and pried loose the back cover of the watch.

He laid the watch on the bench. He watched the quick movements of the tiny wheels and springs. He took out the parts carefully one after another in order to remember them.

He took off another little wheel, then another and another. Soon a pile of tiny wheels and springs and screws lay on the workbench.

130

There was nothing left inside but the face and the hands. Eli took these out, too.

Then he looked up. "I wonder what time it is," he thought. He looked out the window. The position of the sun and the long shadows told him it was getting late!

He felt frightened. His father and Mr. Allen would be back at any moment, and he still had much to do.

Feverishly, he began putting the watch back together piece by piece.

"It's lucky that I remember where each piece belongs," he said, moving his fingers swiftly. "I don't have time to stop and think where each little piece belongs."

He had just put the back on the watch when he heard horses' hoofs turning into the lane and coming toward the house.

"The spoons!" Eli remembered. "I've made only eight of the twelve."

131

There would be no chance now to finish the other four. Mr. Allen would have to hurry home. He would have chores waiting.

Eli held the watch to his ear. It was ticking! He put it back on its peg, just in time. The two riders stopped by the shop door.

"Are my spoons finished?" Mr. Allen asked.

"Eight of them are," said Eli lamely.

"Only eight!" said Mr. Whitney. "What have you been doing with your time, Eli?"

Eli shuffled his feet uneasily. Mr. Allen and his father were displeased. Mr. Whitney said sternly, "When you promise to have something done at a certain time, you should make every effort to have it done. It is easy to see you have wasted time today."

"I will bring the spoons to you the first thing Monday morning," Eli stammered. "Then they won't be very late."

"That's just another promise you cannot keep,"

said his father. "Tomorrow is Sunday, and you cannot work on the Sabbath."

Mr. Whitney reached up and took his watch from the peg. Then he wound it and put it into his pocket. Eli let out a sigh of relief.

Mr. Allen left, disappointed.

Mr. Whitney said, "For one whole week, Eli, you may not use a tool in this shop. Perhaps that will help you keep any promise you may make in the future."

Eli had learned what made the watch tick, but the next week would be dull!

THE WATCH FIXER

Except for the time Eli spent making four pewter spoons, he was not allowed in the shop the next week.

He was glad when the next Saturday morning came, and his father said, "You may go to the shop this morning, Eli, and make a few nails. Now don't waste any time."

Eli worked happily all that day at the forge and anvil. It was late afternoon when a rider turned into the lane.

"That must be the traveling preacher," Eli thought. "He'll have supper with us, and then spend the night with the Allens."

Church services were held in the meeting-house every Sunday, but there was no regular minister. The neighborhood was always glad to see a traveling preacher. Each one spent part of his time with the Whitneys.

The preacher was Mr. Ethan Tucker. Eli liked him right away.

Mr. Whitney came out to meet him. Richard led his horse away to be watered and fed.

While Mrs. Whitney and Betsey cooked supper, Mr. Whitney and Eli showed Mr. Tucker the shop. Visitors always liked to see it.

"You have the most complete set of mechanic's tools I have ever seen!" exclaimed Mr. Tucker. He admired the lathe and the forge and the anvil. He looked at the workbench and the rows of tools ranging above it.

"We make or mend almost anything needed on a farm," Mr. Whitney said proudly.

"It's a pity you cannot repair watches," said Mr. Tucker. "I have an excellent watch in my knapsack, but it will not run. I can find no one who can repair it, and I greatly miss having it on my travels."

Eli overheard. Should he be so bold? Finally he said, "Maybe I can fix your watch."

Mr. Whitney looked at his son in surprise. "You fix a watch!" he cried. "What do you know about watches?"

Eli did not answer. He just said, "I would like to try. I think I can."

Mr. Tucker said, "I should like to have you

135

try. After all, if you fail, I shall be no worse off than I am at present."

"Well, I must say that Eli may do it," said Mr. Whitney. "He has a great knack for doing things mechanically."

Mr. Tucker brought in his watch. Eli was glad to find that it was a round, flat watch just like his father's. He was sure he could fix it.

Soon Mr. Tucker sat down with the family to eat supper. Everyone ate a hearty meal of corn bread, baked beans, and molasses pudding. Mrs. Whitney had cooked enough food to eat the following day, too. She never cooked anything on the Sabbath.

"So many of my meals are cold, and eaten alone on the road," Mr. Tucker said. "I am always pleased to have a real meal."

All through supper Eli kept thinking about the watch. Could he fix it? Suppose he failed?

After supper Eli went straight to the shop. He

wanted to start working. It was still light, so he opened the back of the watch.

He heard Mr. Tucker say good night to Mr. and Mrs. Whitney, and ride off. Eli could return the watch to him after church tomorrow.

Eli pried off three tiny wheels. He laid them and several screws carefully aside. Then he saw the trouble. One tiny screw had slipped out, and one wheel was hanging loose. He replaced them, and put the watch together again. Then he wound it. He held it to his ear.

Tick-tick-tick-tick!

Eli ran to find his father. "I fixed it!" he called loudly. "I fixed it!"

Mr. Whitney said, "I cannot understand how you learned to repair a watch."

Eli wondered whether or not he should tell his father. Someday he would, but it was twenty years before he confessed.

The Homemade Violin

"A STONE BEE!" exclaimed Eli. "I like husking bees and spelling bees and singing bees, but I like stone bees best of all!"

Betsey laughed. "If you were going to a log-rolling next week, you would say that you like that kind of bee best."

"I like any of them," Eli grinned, "as long as there is plenty of food around."

All the Whitneys were excited about this stone bee. It was to be held on Richard Folkes's ten acres. He was married to Verity Allen now. They were living in their own small house on the land Mr. Whitney had given them.

Early in the morning the neighbors gathered, and many strong hands fell to work.

The younger boys helped, too. Eli and Mose picked up smaller stones and piled them around the boundary of Richard's land. The work was very hard but the shouting, singing, and joking made it seem easier.

The men and boys cleared the land. The women and girls talked and set out the food they had brought. They traded patterns and flower seeds. They watched the children run and play beneath the trees.

At noontime all work stopped. Trenchers were filled with the food spread on a long plank table beneath the trees. After a short rest, the men began to work again. As they started back to the field, Mr. Whitney shouted, "We stop at four o'clock. Then the fun begins."

"Does Mr. Harris have his fiddle along to play for us?" asked a neighbor.

"Yes, he has his fiddle all tuned up, ready to go," replied Mr. Whitney.

Eli was glad to hear about the fiddler. Having a fiddler meant that there would be music and dancing.

"There'll be races and games and wrestling, too," said Mose in an excited voice.

The men and boys worked on and on. Finally they cleared the field of most of the boulders. Only the largest ones were left.

"You can grow a lot of corn here next year," Eli said to Richard.

"Yes, without stones this field will grow a lot of corn," replied Richard.

Soon the fun began. The men were tired, but some of them started to race and to wrestle. Others just sat and talked.

The men talked about many things. Some of them talked about the weather, and others talked about growing corn and other crops.

Suddenly Mr. Harris picked up his violin. He drew the bow across the strings and played "Yankee-Doodle Dandy." Feet tapped. Dancing began. Everybody joined in, even the little children who could barely walk.

Mr. Harris fiddled on. The dancers did not get tired, but after a while Mr. Harris did. "Isn't there another fiddler in the crowd?" he asked. He mopped his face.

A strange voice spoke up. Eli looked up and saw a good-looking man walking toward Mr. Harris. "I will take your place for a while," he said.

Mr. Harris was glad to hand over his fiddle to the young man. Eli wondered who the strange young man was.

"It's that nice Mr. Morris," he heard a woman whisper. "He just came from Boston."

Nice Mr. Morris tucked the fiddle under his chin. With a wide smile, he began to play, and how he could fiddle! Even the leaves on the

142

trees seemed to dance. Eli turned to Mose. "I am going to learn to fiddle!"

"But you haven't any fiddle," said Mose.

Eli shrugged his shoulders. "No matter," he said. "I am going to learn. Perhaps someday I can play as well as Mr. Morris."

ELI MAKES A VIOLIN

Eli couldn't forget Mr. Morris' fiddling. He could hear the gay tunes. He could see the dancing feet. He surely wished that he could play.

How could he manage to get a fiddle? A violin was very costly. It would take a long time to save enough money to buy one.

Eli put his hands in his pockets. His fingers touched his jackknife. He could whittle many things. Why couldn't he whittle a violin?

He set about finding the proper wood for whittling one. He told no one except Mose.

"What kind of wood do you want?"

"Some well-seasoned bird's-eye maple, if I can find it," replied Eli.

"There is a fine board of bird's-eye maple in our loft," said Mose. "It is very dry and should be in good shape for whittling."

"Good! Let's get it," cried Eli.

The boys hurried to get the board. "It's a fine board," said Eli, starting to take it home.

By now the boys began to talk about the new term of school, which would start in a few weeks. Both of them had been dreading the new term.

"I've asked Father to let me quit school," said Eli, "but he says no!"

Mose shook his head sadly. "My father says the same thing."

Eli chose a saw to cut down the size of the board. It was much too thick for making the violin the right size.

He tightened the grip of the vise on the board.

"If only Master Phipps were pleasant once in a while," he said. "He must have a mug of vinegar for breakfast every day."

Mose laughed. "Either vinegar or a platter of green persimmons," he said, getting up to leave. "Good luck on making your fiddle."

For several days Eli whittled and steamed and glued. He carved and bent and twisted. Finally he held the finished violin in his hands. It looked like a violin, but would it work?

Eli varnished the new violin carefully, and put it in the sun to dry.

Next he made a bow for the violin. He whittled it and smoothed it and varnished it. Then he put it in the sun to dry.

Finally he had to provide strings for the violin, but he didn't know what to use for strings. What should he use for strings?

He asked his father. "I believe violin strings are made of catgut," said Mr. Whitney.

145

"What is catgut?" asked Eli. "Does catgut come from a cat?"

"No," said Mr. Whitney. "Strangely catgut comes from a sheep. It is the name for the dried intestines of a sheep."

"I think that I'll simply use wire for the strings of my violin," said Eli.

He stretched a fine wire from a peg at the head of the violin over a bridge to a tailpiece at the other end of the violin. Then he tucked the violin under his chin and drew the bow across the wire. The sound made him shiver.

"I guess catgut strings are best," he thought, "but where can I get catgut?"

A PLEASANT SURPRISE!

The first day of school came soon, much too soon for Eli and Betsey.

Eli got out of bed slowly and dressed slowly,

146

taking as much time as he could. He ate breakfast slowly and walked to school slowly.

There would be just one bright spot in the day. He could show his violin to Mose. He held the violin close to his body as he walked to school. He wanted to protect it.

Squirrels crossed his path. Chipmunks darted about. Birds twittered and chirped above him. "These are lucky creatures," he thought. "They don't have to go to school."

The schoolhouse was just ahead. Eli could see a group of boys and girls standing in the yard. He hoped that Mose would be there.

Mose saw Eli coming and ran to meet him so fast that he almost knocked the violin out of Eli's hands.

"Have you heard the news?" he asked, almost too out of breath to speak.

"What news?" asked Eli.

"We have a new schoolmaster!" said Mose.

147

"That's the best news I've heard since I started to school," cried Eli.

"You never know," said Mose, stopping for a moment to talk.

"Never know what?" asked Eli. "I don't quite understand what you mean."

"Well, the next schoolmaster may be worse than the last one," laughed Mose. "We just have to wait to find out."

"Oh, he can't be any worse," said Eli. "He can't be that bad."

"What's that you have?" asked Mose. "Is that your new violin?"

"Yes, it's mine," said Eli handing the violin to Mose. "Do you like it?"

"Can you play it?" asked Mose. "Let's hear you play it."

"Let's take it to our secret hollow by the ravine," said Eli. "Then we can look at it and play it as much as we want to."

The boys hurried to the hollow with the violin. Then Eli tucked it under his chin and drew the bow across the strings. *Squeak, squeak, squeal* went the violin.

Mose put his hands to his ears. "There's something wrong," he said.

"I know," said Eli. "The strings should be made of catgut, but I couldn't get any catgut, so I used an ordinary wire."

"Well, what are you going to do?" asked Mose. "You can't play it the way it is now."

"No, I can't," said Eli, "but I can't do anything about it."

Snap, crack went a twig behind them. "Perhaps I can help you," said a kindly voice.

The boys whirled around to see who was coming. They blinked as they looked. There coming toward them was Mr. Morris.

"We are glad to see you, Mr. Morris," said the boys bashfully.

"Let me see the violin," he said.

Eli handed it to Mr. Morris, who turned it over and examined it closely.

"What was Mr. Morris doing here, near the schoolhouse?" the boys wondered.

His eyebrows were raised in surprise. "You made this yourself?" he asked.

"Yes, sir, I did," replied Eli.

"Very good," said Mr. Morris. "With catgut strings, it should play well. I have a few catgut strings, which you may have. When I come to school tomorrow I will bring the strings and help you put them on your violin."

Eli and Mose stared at each other. "Are you the new schoolmaster?" they asked.

"Yes," said Mr. Morris. "I am taking Master Phipps' place as a schoolmaster."

From this time on Eli was very happy with his work at school. He was praised for the penmanship in his copybook. He was helped

150

with ciphering a problem that bothered him. He was told that his spelling was good.

That evening he walked happily into the kitchen of his home.

"What has happened?" asked Mrs. Whitney in great surprise. "You look just like a cat that has just eaten a bowl of cream."

Eli grinned and told her all about Mr. Morris becoming the new schoolmaster.

The next day Mr. Morris brought the new strings and helped Eli put them on his violin. Then he played a few tunes on the violin.

Eli was happy. Now he had a violin, and a schoolmaster who breakfasted on neither vinegar nor green persimmons.

The Young Patriot

In 1778, TWO YEARS after the signing of the Declaration of Independence, the Colonists were fighting the Revolutionary War.

Some of the Whitneys' neighbors were going to war. They were setting off on foot or horseback to join the Revolutionary Army.

Early one bright June day Eli sat at the workbench busily repairing a violin. He was putting on a new tailpiece.

Hanging on pegs around the wall were several other violins in various stages of repair. Eli had become known as a skillful workman on violins, and neighbors kept sending him violins to repair.

As Eli worked, he could hear the sound of his mother's loom. She was busy wearing woolen cloth, which she and Betsey could use to make heavy cloaks for the soldiers. Most women in the neighborhod were busy weaving cloth and making cloaks for soldiers.

Eli knew that the soldiers would need warm cloaks to wear during the coming winter. He had seen a company of soldiers marching near Westboro. All of them wore tattered cloaks.

"I wish that I could do something more to help win the war," Eli said to himself.

He worked in the field, and helped to raise food for the soldiers, but his mother and Betsey did too. Besides that, he thought, they wove cloth and made clothing for the soldiers. He could not weave cloth and make clothing. What could he do to be of help?

"Here I am spending my time mending fiddles," he thought, "and mending fiddles like this will never help to win the war. I must start to do something else."

Soon Richard came to the door of the shop, carrying a musket on his shoulder. "Good morning, Eli," he said. "I came to say good-by."

"Good morning, Richard," Eli said sadly.

Eli understood that Richard was on his way to join the Revolutionary Army. He knew how hard it was for Richard to go to war. He was leaving his wife, his tiny son, his home, everything that was dear to him. Perhaps he would return, and perhaps he would not.

"I want my son to grow up a free man," said Richard. "That's why I'm going."

He walked to the house to say good-by to Mrs. Whitney and Betsey. Bravely he shook hands, mounted his horse, and rode away. Eli kept watching down the road until Richard was out of sight. Then he returned slowly to the shop and looked solemnly at the fiddles.

154

"Tomorrow I'll go to Westboro," he said. "I surely can find some kind of work there more helpful than mending fiddles."

ELI MAKES NAILS

Early the next morning Eli mounted a horse and headed for Westboro. First he stopped at Mr. Hawkins' blacksmith shop. What a busy place he found!

Customers came and went. Some ordered new muskets and guns, and some bought old weapons to be repaired. Some bought bullets and powder. All came to get firearms for fighting the war.

Mr. Hawkins now had several helpers. All of them hurried here and there in the shop, each doing a special kind of work.

Eli stood about, watching. He wished that he could work for Mr. Hawkins and help to work on muskets and guns.

He wondered whether he could repair muskets and guns in his father's shop. No, because he didn't have the right kind of tools.

At that moment a farmer came in. He did not order a gun and had no weapon to be repaired. He did not order bullets or powder. "I want to buy some nails," he said.

Mr. Hawkins shook his head. "I am sorry, Mr. Ludlow," he said calmly, "but I haven't a single nail in the shop."

"No nails!" cried the farmer. "Why, I have always bought nails from you! I thought that you always kept nails on hand."

"Times are different now," Mr. Hawkins explained. "We have to spend all of our time just making and repairing firearms."

"Well, can't you make just a few nails for me?" begged the farmer. "I need nails to repair the buildings and fences on my farm. Without nails, I can't keep up my farm."

"I am sorry, sir," said Mr. Hawkins, "but I haven't time to make your nails. I have to do what seems best for my country, and that means making and repairing firearms."

Mr. Ludlow shrugged his shoulders and walked away angry. He couldn't understand why Mr. Hawkins wouldn't make a few nails.

Suddenly an idea struck Eli, who had overheard the conversation. He had a forge and an anvil at home. He could make nails for Mr. Hawkins' customers.

Eli called to Mr. Ludlow. "Wait," he said, "I'll make some nails for you!"

Mr. Ludlow turned. "Will you?" He asked. "If you will, I'll certainly be grateful."

"I'll bring you a keg of nails in a very few days," promised Eli.

Mr. Ludlow rode away. Eli grinned happily, mounted his horse, and rode home.

Mr. Whitney already had on hand in his shop a supply of slender rods of iron goods for making nails. Eli located the rods and cut them into the right length for nails. Then he hammered down the heads and sharpened the points.

The news soon spread around the neighborhood that Eli was making nails. Farmers came from all directions to order nails, and Eli had more work than he could do. He worked many long hours each day.

Nails were very scarce during the Revolutionary War, so the farmers were very grateful to Eli. They called him *The Young Patriot*, because he came to their rescue, so that they could raise food to help win the war. They said that he helped to win the war, too.

The Young Mechanic

By the time Eli Whitney reached sixteen years of age, he was known as the best mechanic in Worcester County.

"He can make or mend anything," the people said to one another.

With his forge and anvil, he made nails. On his turning lathe, he made legs and spokes and spindles. He repaired watches and violins and farm machinery.

Eli was busy every day. Finally the time came when, no matter how hard or how long he worked, he couldn't do everything.

"You may quit school now," said his father,

"if you wish more time in the shop. You already know how to read, write, and cipher."

"I don't want to quit school now," said Eli. "I want to get an education."

"You have greatly changed in the way you feel about going to school," laughed his father. "There was a time when you would have jumped at the chance to quit school."

"I am older now and I hope that I'm a little wiser," said Eli. "I think that I'll go to Boston and look for a boy to help me here in the shop. I don't know of any boy around here, who wants to become a mechanic."

Mr. Whitney looked thoughtful. "That will be quite a trip for you to take alone, but it will be a fine experience."

In a few days Eli rode away on his trip to Boston. He stopped at all kinds of shops along the way and looked at everything.

After he reached Boston, he found a place to

stay at an inn. Then he set out to see the sights. He walked up one street and down another. He walked slowly and missed nothing on either side of the street.

By and by Eli passed a bakeshop. The door opened and out came a young lady wearing a new kind of hat. It was far different from the hats that women wore in Westboro.

Suddenly the wind lifted the hat, and took it flying down the street. Eli ran after it.

"Thank you, young man," said the lady, with a smile, as Eli returned the hat.

Eli said nothing, but wondered why the lady hadn't used a hatpin to hold on her hat. Even though there was a wind, she had been trying to hold on her hat with her hand.

"Soon this new kind of hat will be popular in Westboro," thought Eli. "Then there should be a good market for hatpins."

That evening Eli returned to the inn to settle

down for the night. He told the innkeeper that he wanted to hire a boy.

"I know a good boy for you by the name of Thomas Stokes," said the innkeeper. Then he told Eli where he could find the boy.

THE RAIN SHEDDER

Eli and Thomas stood in front of the inn. They were ready to ride back to Westboro, but suddenly a storm had blown up.

"It is just a passing shower," said Eli. "Let's wait here in the doorway until it is over."

The boys waited in the doorway. Soon Thomas saw a man coming down the street, holding a covering somewhat like a big round hat over him. The covering reached over his whole body. He was carrying it by a handle.

"Look at that man!" cried Thomas. "What do you think he is carrying?"

"I don't know," answered Eli. "I have never seen anything like it before."

The man came nearer and the boys could see that he was carrying the strange-looking cover to keep off the rain. Water ran off the edges of the covering and kept him from getting wet. It made a kind of roof over him.

"That's a good idea," said Eli. "It looks like a piece of oiled cloth spread over a big round frame of some kind."

Several small boys were standing in another doorway. They yelled, "There goes old man Mott with his rain shedder."

"It's raining, Mr. Mott," yelled another boy. "Do you know that it's raining? How can you tell when it rains?"

Mr. Mott walked on. He came right up to the doorway where Eli and Thomas were standing. Eli put out his hand to stop him. He wanted to see what the rain shedder was like.

"Please, Mister, may I look at your rain shedder?" he said to the man politely.

"Why, certainly, young man," said Mr. Mott, stopping in the doorway.

Eli took the rain shedder from Mr. Mott and began to open and close it. He was surprised to see how very simply it was made. It consisted only of oiled cloth stretched over ribs of bamboo. The ribs were fastened to an iron ring that ran up and down the handle.

"I believe that rain shedders were first used in China," explained Mr. Mott. "There aren't many of them here in Boston. People make fun of me for having one, but I predict that many people will have them in the future."

"Yes, sooner or later, these rain shedders should catch people's fancy," thought Eli.

"Thank you," he said, handing the rain shedder back to its owner.

"You're quite welcome," said Mr. Mott, hold-

165

ing the umbrella over his head and stepping out into the rain again.

"That rain shedder is an excellent invention, Thomas," said Eli, standing in the doorway of the inn and shaking raindrops from his cloak. "I think that we'll start to make some of them. I'm taking both a helper and useful notions back to Westboro."

NEW AMBITION

Three years later Eli again sat in his father's workshop. He now was nineteen years of age. Thomas Stokes was no longer with him. By now Thomas had gone back to Boston.

Eli was working on a watch. He had parts of the watch strewn on the bench. Propped up before him was a book.

Every once in a while Eli stopped his work and read a few lines in the book. Then, as he

166

began to work again, he tried to think over what he had just read.

"You are still studying, I see," said Mr. Whitney, coming into the shop. "If you keep on so, you'll be an educated man yet."

"I hope so," said Eli. "The older I become, the more I want to be educated."

"Are you still thinking of going to college?"

"Yes, I want to work and save until I have enough money to go to Yale," replied Eli.

"That's fine," said his father. "When you get there, if you need more money, perhaps I can lend you some."

For four long years Eli saved every penny that he could. He worked in the shop. He taught school during the winter months. He worked in the neighbors' fields. All the time, he wanted more and more to go to college.

Finally, when Eli was twenty-three, he had saved enough money to enter Yale College at

New Haven, Connecticut. He was seven years older than most of his classmates, but he didn't care about the difference.

Once, while he was at Yale, a piece of expensive equipment broke down.

"What shall I do?" cried the instructor. "This equipment was made in Europe and I'll have to send it back there to get it repaired. Sending it to Europe and getting it back will take many months. I'm in real trouble."

Young Eli Whitney stepped forward. "Perhaps I can repair it for you," he said.

The instructor raised an eyebrow. "What do you know about equipment of this sort?"

"Not much," said Eli, "but I believe I can soon learn something about it."

"Well," said the instructor, "I have nothing to lose by letting you try."

With the instructor's approval, Eli started to take the piece of equipment apart, just as he had taken his father's watch apart many years before. In a few hours he had the equipment repaired and it was working again, as well as ever.

"The world lost a good mechanic," said the instructor, "when this young Whitney decided to come to Yale."

"Perhaps," said another, standing near by, "but possibly Yale will help him to become a still better mechanic. Education shouldn't hurt him."

"No," said the instructor. "I agree. Education will make him a still better mechanic."

Eli and His Cotton Gin

IN 1792 WHEN Eli was twenty-seven years old, he graduated from Yale. He was offered a position to tutor the children of a wealthy family in Georgia. Immediately after he graduated he left for the South.

Eli was anxious to begin his new work. He needed to work to earn money. After he bought a few new clothes and paid for his transportation, he had no money left.

By coach and by boat, he traveled all the way to Georgia. He was tired when he arrived, but he felt better when he thought of the good salary that he would soon start to earn.

He left his baggage at an inn. Then he asked the way to the house where he was to work. Without stopping to rest or eat, he started to walk down a dusty road. Finally he reached the house and lifted the knocker on the door.

A butler answered Eli's knock. He took one look at Eli's dusty clothes, and said, "Whom do you wish to see?"

When Eli told him, the butler took him into a big parlor to wait.

Eli gasped. He had never seen such a parlor before. It was a huge room, with a high ceiling and tall windows draped with velvet. The tables, chairs, and sofas were plainly the work of great craftsmen. The shining floor was covered with rugs that cost a small fortune.

Soon a man appeared and told Eli curtly that he could expect no job there. His position had already been filled.

Eli was too surprised to speak. He bowed as

politely as he could and said, "Good day." Then he sadly left the house.

Eli went back to the dusty road and started to walk toward the inn. He felt very gloomy, for he had no money, no job, and no friends. He was a long way from home. He almost choked on the dust from the dusty road. Finally he heard a coach coming, but he did not look up. He merely stepped to the side of the road.

The coach was a magnificent vehicle, painted soft blue and trimmed with gold. There were two coachmen on the vehicle.

The coach stopped a few yards ahead. A coachman beckoned, and a woman looked out the window. Eli walked up to the coach, and the woman began to talk with him.

The woman seemed friendly. Eli felt sure that he had seen her somewhere before.

"We are going in your direction," she said with a smile. "Would you care to ride?"

Eli climbed into the coach and sat in the seat
opposite the woman. He was certain that he had
seen her before, but he couldn't tell where. She
asked him where he lived and why he had come

so far from home. She seemed so sympathetic that Eli told her the whole sad story of his trip to her part of the country.

"How discouraging," she said in a sympathetic tone of voice. "Come on home with me. My children need a tutor, and I'm certain that you will make an excellent one for them."

Eli took a deep breath. He could scarcely believe his ears. The lady said nothing more. The coach rumbled on.

"I hope," Eli thought, "that this woman is reliable and means what she says. She is so kind that I find her hard to believe."

He would ask the innkeeper about her. Then he remembered! He would not have to ask anybody about her, for he had met her on the boat coming south. This gracious lady was Mrs. Nathanael Greene, the widow of a famous general in the Revolutionary War!

Mrs. Greene drove Eli to the inn. "I'll return

for you and your baggage in about one hour," she said, waving her hand.

The coach rumbled away, leaving Eli surprised but happy. He had a job after all!

ELI CAN MAKE ANYTHING!

Late that afternoon Eli Whitney arrived at the plantation of Mrs. Nathanael Greene, at Mulberry Grove on the Savannah River.

He was given a large, sunny, and comfortable room. He would earn a good salary as tutor to the Greene children.

Before long Mrs. Greene discovered that Eli was a good mechanic. One evening when she was doing some dainty embroidery work, she suddenly cried, "This frame twists my cloth. It doesn't stretch the cloth as it should."

She held up the twisted cloth that she had just removed from the frame.

"Perhaps I can fix the frame," said Eli. He took the frame and soon had it in good shape again. Mrs. Greene was delighted.

After that Eli mended many of the children's toys and fixed many things in the house. Finally Mrs. Greene gave him a small workshop where he could work with tools.

Mrs. Greene had many parties. Her house was always filled with friends. Mostly they were planters and their families.

One afternoon several planters gathered in the parlor of the Greene house. They were having a lively talk.

"I tell you, friends," said one planter, "what the South needs is a cotton engine."

"You're right," said another. "We can grow large quantities of cotton here in the South, but it costs us too much to take the seed from the fibers. We can't make any money!"

"A cotton engine would make us all rich,"

176

said another dreamily. "It would put all us southern planters back on our feet."

Eli was listening. He remembered that cotton shirts were too expensive for him to wear as a boy. If cotton fibers could be cheaply prepared for spinning, cheap cotton cloth could be made. Cheap cloth would mean cheap shirts, that even poor boys could wear!

All the while Eli said nothing. He knew nothing about cotton, and thought that he should keep still. Suddenly, however, he realized that Mrs. Greene was speaking about him.

"Gentlemen!" she exclaimed. "Mr. Whitney here can make a cotton engine. He is a good mechanic and can make almost anything!"

"A wonderful idea!" cried one planter.

"Success to you!" said another.

One haughty young planter sneered at the idea. "Mr. Whitney may be able to repair embroidery frames and other things," he said, "but he can never invent a cotton engine. It would take a real mechanic to do something like that."

The next day Eli started to work.

He examined some cotton, and found that the seed was indeed hard to take out. He watched Negro workers pull the fluffy fibers from the bolls, and patiently pick out the seeds. They sang to relieve their tiresome jobs.

That evening Eli sat on the veranda in front of the house. He watched the moon, like a silver ship, travel across the deep blue sky overhead. He listened to the songs of Negroes drifting up from their quarters a mile away. He planned a cotton engine in his mind.

The next day he drew pictures of the cotton engine and began to prepare a model. All went smoothly, until he needed some pieces of wire. He set out in search of wire and could find none in town. He tramped from shop to shop looking for wire which he could use.

Eli returned to his shop and wondered what he could do. He had the cotton engine almost finished, but needed the wire to put on the finishing touches.

"What shall I do?" he said to himself as he sat down on a bench. "I can't stop now, when I have the engine almost finished."

He wondered whether he could make some wire, but this would be slow and tedious. Possibly he could order wire from a factory, but this would take weeks or months. He just had to do something to get some wire now.

While he was sitting absorbed in thought, Mrs. Greene's daughter opened the door quietly and walked into the room.

"Please, Mr. Whitney, can you fix my bird cage?" asked the girl. "There are some broken wires on the cage where the birds can get out. I have some wire for you to use."

Eli turned to look, almost speechless!

Eli all but jumped from his chair. In one of her hands the girl carried a bird cage, and in the other, a big roll of wire!

"Where did you get all that wire?" asked Eli, scarcely believing his eyes.

"In the bottom of an old trunk in the attic," replied the girl. "Now will you fix my bird cage?"

"Yes, to be sure," said Eli, "if you will let me have the wire that is left."

"Well, you may have it," said the girl.

Eli repaired the bird cage, and the girl thanked him and left. Then he started to put the wire on the cotton engine. Finally he finished the engine and went to bed happy.

ELI'S CONTRAPTION

The neighboring planters gathered again in the Greene's parlor, this time to see the new cotton engine, which Eli had made.

180

"Will it work?" asked one planter. "If it does, it will revolutionize the South."

"Humph," said the planter who had been doubtful before. "This probably is just some kind of silly contraption."

Eli came in, holding the new cotton engine in his arms. He set it down carefully on a bench close by a large basket of cotton.

The planters gathered around.

The cotton engine was made very simply. It consisted of a cylinder with metal teeth, designed to pull the seeds from the cotton. There were slots on the machine to keep the fibers from going through.

Eli's face was tense. He picked up a handful of cotton and put it in the engine.

He turned the crank at the side. The teeth caught the seeds and pulled them loose from the fibers. The bars kept the fibers from being pulled through.

"The machine works!" yelled one planter joyfully to the others.

"It's too soon to tell," said the doubtful young planter, stepping aside.

Eli picked up more cotton and fed it into the hopper of the machine. The seeds were soon separated from the fibers.

Alas, however, when he put in the next handful of fibers, the machine began to clog. The teeth became filled with lint from the cotton fiber, and would no longer work. Eli started to pick off the lint by hand.

"I told you so!" sneered the doubtful planter. "This thing won't work. You can see that it's just a useless contraption."

Eli picked desperately, trying to remove the lint from the teeth of the machine.

Mrs. Greene, who was standing near by, noticed Eli's troubled face. She turned and noticed something else—a brush on the hearth.

"Here is what you need!" she exclaimed, handing the brush to Eli. He saw what she meant, and held the brush against the turning teeth. It swept off all the lint cleanly.

Eli was very grateful to Mrs. Greene. He bowed to her and said, "Madam, you have made my invention a success."

He rushed back to the shop and hurriedly installed another cylinder with brushes attached to its surface. This cylinder turned in the opposite direction from the first cylinder, and cleared away the lint.

After about two hours, Eli went back to the parlor. He arrived just as the guests were leaving for home.

"Gentlemen!" he cried. "I have added some brushes, and the machine works."

Again Eli tested his cotton engine. This time it worked, and the planters began to cheer. All agreed that it was a success.

The next few years were very hard years for young Eli Whitney. He had invented the cotton gin, which should have made him wealthy, but he was almost penniless!

He set up a factory to manufacture his cotton gin, but his factory ended in failure. He was so poor that he could not pay his workmen.

The chief trouble was that several selfish planters in the South began to manufacture cotton gins. They used Eli's ideas, but didn't pay him for using them.

Finally Eli obtained a patent on his cotton gin, but by that time, the patent was no longer profitable. His chief reward was the honor that came to him for making the growing of cotton successful in the South.

Another Kind
of Invention

ONE DAY several years later Mr. Whitney went to see a wealthy merchant in New England, named Pierrepont Edwards. He wanted to borrow some money for his cotton gin factory.

"I can't loan you any money for making cotton gins, but I might loan you some money for making muskets," said Mr. Edwards. "Why don't you start to make guns?"

Mr. Whitney started to leave. "I'm not a gunsmith," he said. "I don't know how to make guns, but I can make cotton gins."

"Sit down," said Mr. Edwards. "I happen to know that Thomas Jefferson, Secretary of State,

186

is interested in you. He says that you are a good mechanic, and he wants you to make muskets for the Government."

A few weeks later, Mr. Whitney met a Government committee in Philadelphia to talk about manufacturing muskets. The committee wanted him to sign a contract to manufacture ten thousand muskets in ten months.

"Why, that is impossible," said Mr. Whitney. "The way in which muskets are made today, piece by piece, it will take ten years to manufacture ten thousand muskets."

"We can't wait ten years," said the committee. "We need muskets as soon as possible."

"Well, I have an idea," said Mr. Whitney. "I'll start a new way of making muskets, but it will take both time and money."

The committee signed a contract with Mr. Whitney to supply ten thousand guns. Also it agreed to help him borrow some money.

All muskets at this time were made by hand. The parts of each gun were similar to those on other guns, but they were slightly different. The parts of one gun, for instance, couldn't be used on another gun.

Eli Whitney said, "I'll design machines for making the parts of guns. Then the parts for one gun can be used on another gun. Besides the guns will be better."

It took Mr. Whitney about two years to design all the machines that he needed for making guns. By this time he had spent practically all the money that he had borrowed, and he had made only a few hundred guns.

Some people accused Mr. Whitney of spending the money on his cotton gin factory. They knew that he had built a new machine shop, but they couldn't understand what he was doing with it. They couldn't understand why he hadn't made more guns.

The Government called Whitney to Washington for an investigation. There he faced a number of important officials including John Adams, President of the United States, and Thomas Jefferson, who by now had become Vice-President. The group also included General Simeon North of the United States Army.

Mr. Whitney took with him to Washington several boxes filled with parts for guns. He had made the parts with the special machines which he had designed.

General North accused Mr. Whitney of failing to keep his contract. He asked him why he had delivered only four hundred muskets.

Mr. Whitney explained how he had invented and built special machines for making the parts of guns. He explained that these steps had taken time, but that he felt they were necessary. Now he had reached the point where he could make guns quickly and accurately.

To help show what he meant, Mr. Whitney opened up the boxes of gun parts. "I have here all the parts needed for making ten muskets," he said. "General North, I'll put a gun together for you, if you will pick out the parts."

"Why I don't know which parts belong with each gun," replied General North.

"Just select any one of each kind of part," said Mr. Whitney. "All pieces of each kind are alike. They'll fit any gun."

The general picked out some pieces, and Mr. Whitney put them together. Soon he had the gun completed, and held it up for everyone to see. Then he loaded the gun and shot at a target through an open window.

The members of the committee could scarcely believe their eyes. They had never seen a gun assembled so rapidly before. "Now that I have machines," said Mr. Whitney, "I can make as many guns for you as you want."

The years passed and Eli Whitney became known as a great man. He had set up a new kind of factory equipped with special machines and he started a new way of making things.

People traveled from many parts of the world to see Whitney's gun factory. It was the first gun factory where all the parts were made by machines. Every part of one gun was made exactly like the same part of another gun. The parts could be interchanged.

Eli Whitney is remembered for starting the method of making interchangeable parts. This method, which he started, helped manufacturing to grow and to become a great business.

People today honor Eli Whitney as a great inventive genius. First, he invented the cotton gin, which brought him honor without money. Second, he invented the method of making interchangeable parts, which made him a successful pioneer manufacturer.

More About This Book

WHEN ELI WHITNEY LIVED

1765   ELI WHITNEY WAS BORN IN MASSACHUSETTS.

Massachusetts was one of the thirteen colonies ruled by England.

The population of the colonies was about 2,660,000.

1765–
1773   ELI HELPED ON THE FARM.

The English Parliament passed the Stamp Act, 1765.

The Boston Massacre occurred, 1770.

The "Boston Tea Party" took place, 1773.

1773   ELI STARTED TO SCHOOL.

The First Continental Congress met, 1774.

Paul Revere made his famous ride, 1775.

The first battle of the Revolutionary War was fought at Lexington, Massachusetts, 1775.

The Second Continental Congress met, 1775.

The Declaration of Independence was signed, July 4, 1776.

1777–
1788   ELI BECAME A NOTED MECHANIC.

Cornwallis surrendered at Yorktown, 1781.

The peace treaty with England was signed ending the Revolutionary War, 1783.

The Constitutional Convention met to frame the United States Constitution, 1787.

The Northwest Territory was established, 1787.

1788–
1792   ELI WENT TO YALE.

George Washington became the first President, 1789.

The Banking system in the United States was established, 1791.

Kentucky was admitted as a state, 1792.

1793   YOUNG WHITNEY INVENTED THE COTTON GIN.

Anthony Wayne defeated the Indians in the Battle of Fallen Timbers, 1794.

Tennessee was admitted as a state, 1796.

John Adams became President, 1797.

1798   ELI WHITNEY BEGAN TO MANUFACTURE MUSKETS.

Thomas Jefferson was President, 1801-1809.

194

George Washington died, 1799.

The United States bought the Louisiana Territory, 1803.

Lewis and Clark explored the Northwest, 1804-1806.

James Madison was President, 1809-1817.

The War of 1812 was fought, 1812-1815.

Florida was purchased from Spain, 1819.

1825 ELI WHITNEY DIED.

There were 24 states in the Union.

James Monroe was President.

The population of the country was about 11,000,000.

DO YOU REMEMBER?

1. How did Eli try to catch the crows in the cornfield?
2. What did he make for his mother's birthday?
3. Who was Richard Folkes?
4. What work did Richard do for Eli's father?
5. What happened at the corn husking bee?
6. How did Eli and Mose Hartley become friends?

7. Who was Amby Benedict and why did the Whitneys like to have him come?

8. What kind of deal did Amby make with Eli?

9. Why did Eli not want to go to school?

10. Where did Eli and Mose Hartley spend the noon recess at school?

11. How did Eli finally get his jackknife?

12. What did Eli watch the blacksmith in Westboro put on a horse?

13. Who was the new schoolmaster and why did Eli like him?

14. How did Eli serve as a patriot during the Revolutionary War?

15. Where did Eli decide to go to college?

16. Where did he go to become a tutor after he graduated from college?

17. How did he come to try to make a "cotton engine" in the South?

18. Why did he never make any money from manufacturing cotton gins?

19. Why did he start later on to make muskets for the government?

20. What new method of manufacturing did he start?

196

IT'S FUN TO LOOK UP THESE THINGS

1. What is a blacksmith shop?
2. Why is iron heated to make things?
3. What is a lathe and how is it used?
4. Where is most cotton raised in our country?
5. What do you find in a cotton boll?
6. What was *Poor Richard's Almanack?*
7. How were spinning wheels once used?

INTERESTING THINGS YOU CAN DO

1. Find a boll of ripe cotton and pick out the seeds by hand. Notice how difficult it is to separate the seeds from the fibers.
2. Collect small samples of cotton cloth and mount them on a piece of cardboard. Include samples of different colors.
3. Make a list of other things made from the cotton plant besides cloth and tell for what each is used.
4. Make a drawing of cotton bales to show how cotton is prepared for market.
5. Bring to class pictures of old muskets like those used during the Revolutionary War.

OTHER BOOKS YOU MAY ENJOY READING

George Washington: Boy Leader, Augusta Stevenson. Trade and School Editions, Bobbs-Merrill.

Johnny Tremaine, Esther Forbes. Houghton Mifflin.

Nathanael Greene: Independent Boy, Howard Peckham. Trade and School Editions, Bobbs-Merrill.

Paul Revere: Boy of Old Boston, Augusta Stevenson. Trade and School Editions, Bobbs-Merrill.

Spy in Old Williamsburg, Isabelle Lawrence. Rand-McNally.

INTERESTING WORDS IN THIS BOOK

almanac (ôl′má năk) : booklet listing days, weeks, and months, hours of sunrise and sunset, dates of changes in the moon, and often predicting changes in the weather

anvil (ăn′vĭl) : iron block on which pieces of metal are hammered into shape

blacksmith (blăk′smĭth′) : man who works with iron in a blacksmith shop

boll (bōl) : seed pod of a plant

bramble (brăm′b′l) : prickly shrub, such as a blackberry or a raspberry bush

198

chaise (shāz) : two-wheeled covered cart or carriage, pulled by one horse

cipher (sī'fẽr) : use figures in solving an arithmetic problem

cocklebur (kŏk''l bûr) : rough seed-vessel of the cockle plant, often found in fields of grain

cooper (kōōp'ẽr) : person who makes or repairs barrels, casks, buckets, tubs, and other containers made of wood

fiber (fī'bẽr) : thread-like substance obtained from certain plant and animal products

homespun (hōm'spŭn') : cloth made of yarn which has been prepared at home

hominy (hŏm'ĭ nĭ) : hulled corn, used for food

husking (hŭsk'ĭng) : stripping the husks from ears of corn

indigo (ĭn'dĭ gō) : blue dye, now made artificially, but once obtained from plants, especially the indigo plant

jackknife (jăk'nīf') : large pocket knife

lathe (lāth) : machine for turning materials to shape them or polish them

mechanic (mė̆ kăn'ĭk) : person skillful in the use of tools and machines

pewter (pū'tẽr) : metallic substance made of tin, copper, and several other metals

plaster (plás'tẽr) : kind of salve spread on cloth, ready to apply to the body

porcupine (pôr'kŭ pīn) : kind of animal having stiff, sharp spines on its body

rainbow (rān'bō') : bow or arc of colors caused by the sun shining on moisture in the sky

ravine (rȧ vēn') : hollow worn by a creek or other small stream

sapling (săp'lĭng) : young slender tree

sawhorse (sô'hôrs') : kind of frame or rack on which wood rests while being sawed

shaving (shāv'ĭng) : thin slice or strip of wood pared off with a knife or plane

spine (spīn) : stiff, sharp-pointed projection, as a thistle or thorn

trencher (trĕn'chẽr) : wooden plate or platter on which to carve or serve food

washboard (wŏsh'bōrd') : grooved board used for washing clothes

wheelwright (hwēl' rīt') : man who makes or repairs wheels for carriages and wagons

whittle (hwĭt''l) : pare shavings from wood

200

Childhood
OF FAMOUS AMERICANS

COLONIAL DAYS

JAMES OGLETHORPE, *Parks*
JOHN ALDEN, *Burt*
JOHN PETER ZENGER, *Long*
JOHN SMITH, *Barton*
MYLES STANDISH, *Stevenson*
PETER STUYVESANT, *Widdemer*
POCAHONTAS, *Seymour*
PONTIAC, *Peckham*
SQUANTO, *Stev*
VIRGINIA DA
WILLIAM BRA
WILLIAM PEN

DEWITT CLINTON, *Widdemer*
DOLLY MADISON, *Monsell*
ELI WHITNEY, *Snow*
ELIAS HOWE, *Corcoran*
FRANCIS SCOTT KEY, *Stevenson*
HENRY CLAY, *Monsell*
JAMES FENIMORE COOPER, *Winders*
JAMES MONROE, *Widdemer*
JOHN AUDUBON, *Mason*
JOHN FITCH, *Stevenson*

arbach

STRUGO
INDEPE

ANTHONY V
BEN FRANK
BETSY ROSS
CRISPUS AT
DAN MORG
ETHAN ALL
FRANCIS MA
GEORGE RO
GEORGE WA
ISRAEL PUT
JOHN HANC
JOHN PAUL
MARTHA W
MOLLY PIT
NATHAN H
NATHANAE
PATRICK H
PAUL REVE
TOM JEFFER

ENT

sbee

EARLY
GROWT

ABIGAIL A
ALEC HAMI
ANDY JACK
BLACK HAWK, *Cleven*
DAN WEBSTER, *Smith*

SIMON KENTON, *Wilkie*
TECUMSEH, *Stevenson*

*
J
92
W

HARDEMAN COUNTY PUBLIC LIBRARY
TUESDAY, WEDNESDAY 9:30 TO 5:30
THURSDAY, FRIDAY 12:30 TO 5:30
SATURDAY 9:30 TO 3:30
PHONE: 663 - 8149

HARDEMAN COUNTY LIBRARY
QUANAH, TEXAS